MODERN FURNISHINGS FOR THE HOME

2

William J. Hennessey

Eliza Dornin Hennessey
Associate

REINHOLD PUBLISHING CORPORATION
New York

CONTENTS

INTRODUCTION

In 1952 the first volume of *Modern Furnishings For The Home* was published. To our knowledge it was the first book of its kind—the first comprehensive catalog devoted exclusively to available contemporary merchandise. Its wide acceptance by professional and consumer alike was most gratifying. Here, at last, was a short cut to comparisons and evaluations of a style that was steadily growing in popularity and changing the nation's living patterns. Heretofor, architect, decorator and homeowner had to depend on numerous manufacturer's brochures or time-consuming walks around display showrooms before making decisions. Each item shown in the book had been carefully selected for excellence of design and structure and, above all, with the hope that it would be available to the homeowner for years to come. Though the average manufacturer hesitates to predict such longevity, we are happy to report that the great majority of our selections are on the market today.

Four years have passed, and modern design continues its tremendous success story. It is more widely accepted today than ever before. A recent survey of 251 retailers showed that, in many instances, it is even outranking its traditional competition in selling power. During these past years, a great many new manufacturers and designers have entered the field, adding fresh imagination and interpretations to the already overwhelming output of contemporary home furnishings. Selection becomes even more difficult. Because of our initial success, publisher and author, alike, felt that a second volume, one that would cover those designs that have appeared during the past four years, was in order. As before we have made our selections with great care, noting new trends and techniques and grouping each item for easy comparison. Because rugs and carpets today are such a vital part of the contemporary scene, we've devoted a chapter to them.

What direction, then, has modern design taken during the past few years? Perhaps the most notable trend is towards greater simplicity, smaller scale and greater comfort. Architecture and new living habits may account for this. We live in homes that become smaller and smaller. To give them stature, furnishings must be scaled down, low and clean of line. Because too we stay at home and entertain more, thanks to television and radio, we demand furniture that is comfortable to sit on for long periods of time.

A careful checkup on the contents of the book will show more flush-fitting cases and multi-purpose units. Many are co-ordinated for more flexibility of arrangement, since today's rooms are often called upon to serve double-duty. In keeping with our desire for easy maintenance, ornament is out and in its place we have contrasting woods, plastics and gleaming touches of metal for added eye-appeal. Surfaces, for the most part, expose the natural grain of the wood and are protected by a semi-gloss, resistant finish.

This same desire for simplicity is noted, too, in today's lamps. Gone is the "tortured" look of other days and in its place we note an emphasis on more graceful lines, bright metal finishes and more flexibility of use. As contrast to the straight, clean lines of the furniture, fabrics and rugs offer exciting new textures and patterns. Scale, here too, has been carefully controlled to fit into the all-over decorative scheme. On the whole, new modern furnishings have a more relaxed look, a serenity that will transform any room into a fitting refuge from the high-tensioned work-a-day world outside.

By popular request, we've included the Foreword of the first book together with some outstanding examples selected at the time. We hope that, in its small way, it will give those who read it a better understanding of the forces behind the modern movement, to evaluate it in terms of more traditional schools and to appreciate its contributions to a better 20th century way of living.

WILLIAM J. HENNESSEY

May, 1956

FOREWORD

This is a catalog of a style—compiled with the sincere conviction that a definite need exists today for a single, comprehensive reference guide where the individual and personal schools of Modern design may be compared and properly evaluated.

The output of contemporary home furnishings during the past few years has been staggering. Much that we see is excellent, of sound design, intent and craftsmanship. Much, however, depending on surface values and showmanship in its bid for attention, seems destined, like all sham, for early obsolescence. Intelligent selection by both professional and layman becomes increasingly more difficult.

How, then, can the real worth of any particular piece be judged? What yardstick will tell us the good from the mediocre?

Perhaps when we realize that all good design is an honest reflection of the social, economic, and emotional changes of its times, we gain the real key to objective evaluation. Modern design is no exception. Its aims are very real; its roots run deep—far into the industrial revolution of the past century. Modern has benefited from its very start because of the infinite possibilities of the machine and its promise of mass production. Modern design is the creation of certain isolated groups, of both the past and present centuries, who strove for better co-relation between artist and craftsman, who turned their backs on the outmoded cliches and limitations of Classicism and Medievalism, the more honestly to reflect their own civilization!

At the turn of the 19th century few individuals seemed conscious of the immense potentials of the age, only a few understood the aims of Eli Whitney "to substitute correct and effective operations of machinery for that skill of the artist which is acquired after long experience." Certainly the Academicians, especially in America, would have nothing to do with this heresy and continued to follow patterns set by other generations, covering their buildings and furnishings with thick coatings of traditional icing. Even when steel and iron were introduced into homes, on stoves or bathroom fixtures, their surfaces received the same treatment. Only in the field of engineering, particularly in the realm of bridge design, do we see steel used honestly and unadorned. In fact, during the entire 19th century, architecture and engineering remained worlds apart.

In 1833, the introduction of cheap, machine-made nails made possible lightweight, balloon house construction and eliminated the need for heavy, mortise-and-tenon framework. Only the non-professional recognized its worth and only in rural areas did it receive wide acceptance. Far-sighted men like Lewis F. Allen, a farmer with no formal training, were advocating a philosophy that is reflected today in the work of our best contemporary designers. In his "Rural Architecture," published in 1852, he states, "good taste depended on fitness of purpose for which it was intended and the harmony of its various parts." Again, in the same book, we note that "no architecture could be really bad if utility is duly consulted and complied with."

Towards the latter part of the 19th century we

George Nelson

find more and more of these logical thinkers, in nearly every case a non-professional, striving for a more honest expression of his times, showing an awareness to the rapidly developing technologies of their day. Harriet Beecher Stowe, together with her sister Catherine, attempted a house plan that put purpose before established style. Its utilities were grouped together in a central core, ventilated by a series of flues, allow-

ing the maximum of well-lighted exterior wall space in the principal rooms. The cooking part of the kitchen was isolated by a glass wall in order to prevent the escape of heat and odors. In the main living room, these inventive ladies placed a rolling screen, one that reached from one wall to the opposite, a screen that could be wheeled about for more flexibility in dividing the two parts of the room. Whether any of these houses were built is doubtful—they were designed for mass production—but they did point a direction that still inspires leading Modern architects.

The octagon houses of Orson S. Fowler, many of which were built along the Hudson River in the late 1800's, followed the same general plan and placed the more mechanical elements in a central core. Their wedge-shaped rooms, however, presented decorating difficulties which prevented wide acceptance.

This search for a more flexible floor plan became a characteristic of American houses during the 19th century, even among avowed traditionalists. It was especially true of houses built during the Greek Revival of the 1820's when sliding doors came into extensive use. This ingenious method of uniting or dividing two areas remained uniquely American and was considered a novelty by visiting Europeans when they first saw it displayed at the Chicago World Fair of 1893.

Perhaps the greatest single contribution to the modern home furnishings field came from the many Shaker communities that dotted our mid- and upper-Eastern seaboard. These nonconformists rejected the established translation of beauty in favor of a living pattern where "function dictated form." They welcomed the machine and used it in their daily tasks wherever possible. Their houses were severe to the point of austerity, unlike those of the Pennsylvania Dutch, completely unpainted, and their furnishings, admired more today than are their ornament-ridden contemporaries, had simplicity, lightness, and clarity of line. The aims of these furnishings were in complete harmony with the Shaker concept of equalitarian democracy and, because of their sensitiveness to the technological advances of the times, they have far outlasted the artificialities of the then-popular idiom. A close study of many designs in this book will show our present day indebtedness to this early Shaker influence.

Though we see, throughout the 19th century, no concerted effort towards a logical expression of the times, forces usually untrained but aware, were at work to fire later generations into action. Though new materials were constantly coming into being and manufacturing methods offered greater facilities for mass production, engineers alone were exploiting them for their basic functional worth. Architects and most designers, on the other hand, remained on safe ground and looked for inspiration abroad, continuing to import our culture. Unfortunately, they were to continue this practice for the first twenty-five years of the 20th century!

Meanwhile, in Europe, during the 19th century, the search for new expression was more organized and followed nationalistic trends. For example, during the middle 1800's, we find an aesthetic-minded group in England, headed by William Brown, Rossetti, Philip Webb, Burne-Jones and others, revolting against a dead classicism which dominated most creative thinking. Their aims were the return to naturalism and the Medieval concept of humanity, nature, and brotherhood. The revolt succumbed in a mire of artistic obscurities. It did, however, bequeath a yearning for more honest expression, fine craftsmanship, and applied art where undisguised form was influenced by function. It inspired others, notably William Morris, to found the "Arts and Crafts" school whose aim was a better integration of the efforts of artist and craftsman. The school depended on individual handiwork and, though the possibilities of the machine were completely ignored, produced a new type of furniture, stiff and "cottagey" in appearance, one that became well known both here and abroad.

In France, L'Art Nouveau, based on a naturalistic rather than a classical approach, produced one figure whose impact on the work of later designers was considerable. Henry van de Velte, alive to the possibilities of the machine, recognized the importance of the engineer as a creative designer and insisted that new materials—reinforced concrete, aluminum, and steel—cried for new forms of structural expression. His four completely furnished rooms, displayed at the 1895 Paris Exhibition, established a style. It was welcomed by the avant garde and copied endlessly throughout Europe. Though confused in design and "arty" in appearance, it was the first tangible expression of the revolt against tradition. In 1902, van de Velte accepted the directorship of the Weimar Academy of Arts and Crafts in Germany. This school, based on a new interpretation of the applied arts, was followed by others and, in 1907, Herman Muthesius, seeking a more logical correlation between the "machine style" and the "arts and crafts" of William Morris, founded the Deutsche Werkbund. Though he and other leaders of the school strove for quality through mass production and a proper division of labor, they were unsuccessful in any attempt to absorb the true spirit of engineering in their art. The basic weakness of the Werkbund lay in the romantic individuality of architects, sculptors, and artists.

In 1896, we find the secession being organized, in Austria, by Josef Hoffman, Roller, Klimt, Moser and others. These leaders sought a better consolidation of the active forces in art, education, and production. The Wiener Werkstatte which followed, in 1903, formulated the first coherent style, one that tremendously affected the design and decoration of houses throughout Europe until the outbreak of World War I. During the same period similar experiments were taking place in the Scandinavian countries, largely through co-operative associations. The results of these early labors, both in architecture and home furnishings, continue to inspire contemporary thinking. Its light appearance and weight, its direct use of materials, old or new, and its lack of ornament, held the same functional beauty and intent that we associate with Shaker design.

After World War I economic and emotional forces overlaying Europe acted as stimuli for better understanding between artist, craftsman, and engineer. In 1919, Walter Gropius, an architect whose experiments at pre-fabrication and whose office building at the Werkbund Exposition in Cologne in 1914, had established him as a leader in the new movement, founded the Bauhaus, a combination of the Weimar Art Academy and the Weimar Arts and Crafts school. Here the student was taught each subject by two teachers—one, an artist, the other a master craftsman. This revolutionary system created an ambidextrous approach and, in the end, was largely responsible for the functional design we know today.

By the time the Bauhaus moved to new quarters at Dessau, in 1925, a new generation of teachers had been trained, each a creative artist, craftsman, and industrial engineer. Thus the original dual instructor method could be abandoned. It was a prolific period, a time spent in endless experiments for modern functional expression. Out of it came many objects and home furnishings familiar to audiences today—steel furniture, modern fabrics, modern lighting fixtures among them. The Bauhaus also made its influence felt in architecture. A building, according to Bauhaus standards, should be "clear, organic, whose inner logic will be radiant and naked, unencumbered by lying facades and trickeries; we want an architecture adapted to our world of machines, radios and fast motor cars, an architecture whose function is clearly recognizable in the relation of its forms." Lewis F. Allen, back in 1852, would certainly have endorsed such aims.

A roll call of instructors at the Bauhaus during these productive years from 1919 to 1923 would include many whose impact on the living patterns of the world is still felt. Among them were such leaders as Lyonel Fieninger, Johannes Itten, Adolf Mayer, Paul Klee, Wassily Kandinsky and Lazlo Moholy-Nagy. At the time, however, these men and their work were unfamiliar to most Americans. It took the Paris Exposition of Decorative Arts in 1925 to throw into sharp relief the backwardness of American applied art. The United States had nothing to show!

At the turn of the century, only a handful of American designers seemed conscious of the significance of the industrial and economic revolution. Louis Sullivan and Frank Lloyd Wright were perhaps the most influential, but even the straight-forward approach to skyscraper design of the former and the logical principles underlying the design of the latter's houses in the Mid-west affected the prevalent archeological approach of other designers hardly at all. A later generation does now fully appreciate their genius and the important contributions made by each in the realm of contemporary design and architecture. Wright's pioneering energies are still apparent in his recent residential and commercial designs.

Perhaps the greatest moving force to shape the destinies of American design in the first twenty-five years of the 20th century was the Chicago World's Fair of 1893. Its Classic revival, its complete misunderstanding of the basic qualities of

Gio Ponti

Paul McCobb

Ico Parisi

steel construction, its over-elaboration brought on a wave of romanticism that lasted until 1925. During that period, houses and home decoration were strictly "out of the book"; the few who deviated from these set rules were considered radical and visionary.

Americans, too, suspected the International Style of architecture, named so because its ingredients—steel, concrete, and glass were everywhere available. Homeowners found its bare, unadorned walls and angular forms too clinical for their palates; the economy of its construction and the logic of its floor plan affected them not a whit. Eye-appeal alone guided the popular taste.

The turning point in American design expression arrived in 1925 when the few Americans, fortunate enough to have attended the Paris Exposition, returned with glowing reports about the new excitement uncovered there. Modern furniture and furnishings began coming to these shores soon afterward, but the market was limited, and costs were prohibitive. However, these first importations acted as a stimulus for many American designers who had become dissatisfied with established patterns. Fortunately, too, many European creative designers came to these shores and some of them became instructors in our schools and universities. The effect these people had on the progress of modern applied design here was far-reaching and cannot be discounted.

Perhaps enthusiasm for the new idiom ran too high during these early days. Externals were often stressed in an attempt at release from outmoded cliches and forms. Materials, old and new, were tortured for the sake of appearance and function was often obscured. The tubular metal chair, prime symbol of revolt, was copied ad nauseam everywhere until, for a time, it seemed condemned by its very success. This was a period of trial and error. Not until the years 1930 to 1940 do we find a more relaxed approach to the problem—a more functional understanding of its aims. Techniques, characteristically American, become evident; we began substituting native woods, especially plywoods, since these were as malleable as tubing and lacked its clinical qualities. Motion and posture studies, carried out by manufacturers as well as designers, made us con-

scious of the many and varied attitudes assumed by the human body. Drafting rooms became laboratories for testing new materials, forms, and methods. New products—there seemed to be no end of them—were accepted or rejected according to their abilities to answer basic needs. A better understanding developed between designer and architect, resulting often in collaboration between the two. The industrial engineer, combining the abilities and functions of architect, artist, craftsman, and engineer, made his appearance. Modern design began to attract a larger audience.

However, no style, no matter how logical and necessary, can properly develop without a mass market. This is especially true today when the machine, to be effective and economical, must produce in enormous quantities. Since they reached a limited market, manufacturers were loath to add this new style form to their established lines. The mass market for contemporary design finally came into being when rising building costs and an acute building shortage, brought on by World War II, highlighted the need for a different pattern in home living.

Rising building and labor costs also accentuated the inadequacies of the standard house plan. Houses became increasingly smaller with rooms hopelessly inadequate. The adoption of a new kind of house with a flexible, open plan and a minimum number of fixed, rigid partitions came into being and gained nationwide support from architects, builders, and public alike. Such planning added stature to the smallest of houses. We began designing our houses from the inside rather than for exterior appearance. Family living patterns were analyzed in an attempt to evolve form through function. Rooms were designed for double-duty in order to make every square inch pay off in usefulness and livability. The modern house was developing through the same processes that have inspired all phases of sound design.

During the past ten years modern and transitional houses have been erected throughout the country at the rate of eight hundred thousand or more a year. Even the poorest designed of these millions of new houses provides a good background for modern home furnishings. Their owners, usually young married people, have an

Eero Saarinen

open-minded awareness to all things modern, be it motor car, refrigerator, or day bed. They are interested in the future and mold their home living patterns in that direction. In addition, modern light-weight, compact pieces save space and are easy and cheap to maintain. They also adapt themselves to mobility of arrangement so necessary in restricted areas.

Here, then, was the mass market for modern home furnishings, so long awaited and so important to its survival. Department stores and manufacturers sensed its importance and, during the past few years, have given it greater display and production. Magazines and museums satisfied the growing interest with bigger spreads and exhibitions. Everyone realized from the start that, for the most part, this was a budget-minded market and consequently sights were set in that direction. Recently there have been increasing indications that the aim of quality-at-a-price in the field of contemporary design has been reached. This fact will inevitably bring modern home furnishings an even wider acceptance.

Modern design does not follow any set pattern in appearance; rather it represents many individual and personal techniques. Each one, however, has the same objective—to satisfy the unique demands of today with the materials and know-how available. Each treats materials honestly and intelligently, allowing function to dictate form. From the past the secrets of fine craftsmanship have been borrowed. The present affords new materials and tools with which to work. The future augurs well because more and more architects are joining the ranks of furniture designers. Moreover, all designers realize now more than ever the importance of better integration between a house and its component parts.

The output of contemporary merchandise during the past few years has been staggering. Every new Home Furnishings Market finds more and more lines being added; many manufacturers have placed their entire emphasis in the modern field. Until now, to keep pace with this rapidly expanding output, architects and decorators were dependent on individual manufacturer's catalogs or endless rounds of department stores and showrooms. Such catalogs, excel-

Charles Eames

Knoll Planning Unit

Hendrik Van Keppel and Taylor Green

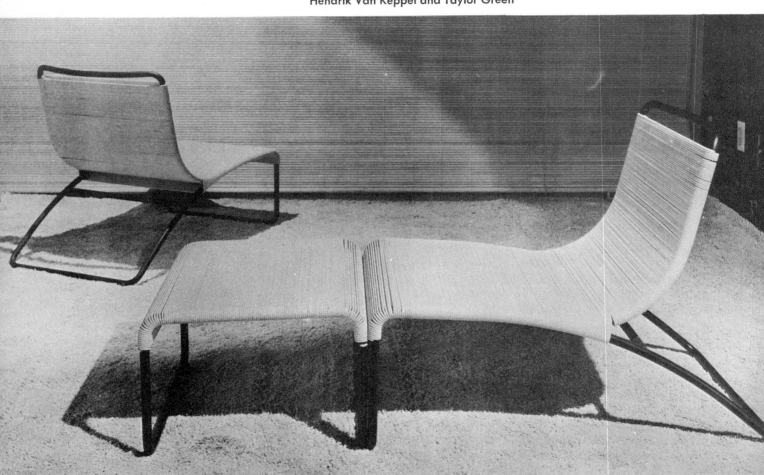

lent though many of them are, naturally are limited in scope. Also, to keep pace with the constant flow of contemporary merchandise they become more and more numerous, often confusing rather than clarifying the processes of objective comparison.

It is no trade secret that steering a client around the wholesale-retail circuit is a grueling procedure, physically wearing and time-consuming. Therefore to architect, decorator, and client alike, this book is offered as a short-cut, an easy way to introduce and simplify comparative evaluations.

We hope, too, that it will be equally instructive to consumer and student. To the former it will bring a better understanding of the principles underlying good modern design, giving a wider acquaintanceship with leading designers and manufacturers whose efforts are moulding a new living pattern not only in America but throughout the entire world. It will afford them, too, a more extensive selection of merchandise, especially that which is not available through their own retail sources. For those dreaming of adding or adapting modern designs into their homes or apartments, the sizes and finishes indicated with each piece will allow a chance for better integration with their present furnishings.

Since individual techniques stand side by side on its pages, analytical comparisons are offered students of both architecture and design and afford an easy chance to weigh merits and discover directions. It will allow them, too, a realistic approach to their school problems, bring them into closer contact with merchandise already being manufactured and of proven quality. We also offer the book as a source of inspiration and encouragement to all those who, in the future, plan to dedicate their creative energies towards a better, more honest expression of 20th century living.

Naturally, due to production limitations, every piece of modern furniture, every lighting fixture, lamp, or fabric design could not be included. The task of selecting and rejecting was not an easy one. Final choice and inclusion depended, first of all, on the satisfactory solution to a human need. This, combined with an intelligent use of materials and expert craftsmanship, indicated timelessness and importance. Since established form, especially a commercially successful one, always has its copyists, credit was given, wherever possible, to its originator. Choice, too, depended on a reasonable guarantee from designer or manufacturer that the merchandise would be available for years to come, a factor extremely necessary to the real worth of any practical reference guide. This eliminated many foreign designs, although some of European origin, now being manufactured in this country, were included. Most of the designs and designers are completely American with a clear idea of this country's needs and are adapted to the scale of today's home living.

The furnishings illustrated have been divided into eight categories, each representing a basic need. If a piece had a dual-purpose, its primary function dictated the heading under which it was included. In turn, designs included under each main division have been arranged accord-

Irving Sabo

ing to a specific special function. For example, all dining tables are grouped together, all coffee tables follow one another, for easy comparison. Even under Fabrics, abstracts, textures, stylized natural forms, and weaves have each been placed together, according to scale, so that their individual merits can be studied more logically.

In turn every piece of merchandise is accompanied by the catalog number of its manufacturer, together with descriptive data relating its size, material and finish. In every case, credit has been given designer and manufacturer. If further information is desired, individual manufacturer's addresses are listed in the back of the book. Prices and retail outlets had, by necessity, to be omitted since these are subject to constant change.

More than 480 separate pieces or designs have been included, each representative of the best European as well as American schools of creative thought. Each exemplifies the basic concept of all good contemporary design—undisguised form influenced by function, together with an intelligent use of materials and fine craftsmanship. All are real, no dream promises of the future; all answer the unique demands of our times in terms of advanced technology and know-how!

A thorough analysis of the pages brings to light a few characteristics that are common to all good contemporary design, one that definitely points a direction. Every piece of furniture, no matter how indicative it may be of an individual designer's technique, is low and light in appearance. Each is completely devoid of extraneous decoration, allowing material and joinery to exploit their natural and functional beauty. Finishes and fabrics, whether for upholstery or curtains, are resistant to dirt and wear and easy to maintain. Metals, when used, are thin and clean of line, rid of Victorian curlecues so often associated with them in the past. Lightness, whether in wood or metal, is in complete sympathy with the aim for a more spacious, airy appearance in the modern house, one that eliminates an atmosphere of clutter in the open plan where areas flow naturally into one another. Lightness of weight is also in keeping with the mobility of arrangement so desired when rooms are used for more than one purpose.

We find, too, a better feeling of integration

between various elements. Desks, cabinets, and even beds are designed with an eye to more flexible arrangement. Many pieces, notably storage units and room dividers, possess additional architectural qualities and often may be substituted for rigid wall construction. Because they are designed on a unit basis such pieces are interchangeable and offer infinite variety of arrangement. Room dividers are particularly acceptable in today's house since they are not only mobile but offer area separation without the confining limitations of the standard wall. Storage units, no matter how used, become a part of a room's over-all pattern, eliminate the need for conventional closet doors which often restricted a designer's scope and, by the very beauty of their natural finishes, have taken a definite place in architectural planning.

Tables take on a new importance in the modern home. Not only must they be adaptable for many purposes, but, at the same time, they must be light in construction, stackable, knock-down, and resistant to all sorts of wear. Their heights have been carefully adjusted to meet specific demands and their shapes, often free-form or with rounded corners, planned for easy access about a room. We notice a trend towards the round dining table, a reflection of our present-day, informal family life. Not only does such a table offer more intimate seating arrangements at meals but it allows for more efficient passing of dishes in the servantless house. Again, in its dual-purpose role, the round table is a perfect gathering spot for family, or social get-togethers.

We find, too, a new emphasis on the coffee table in modern design. Often the focal point in our decorative scheme of things, designers have given it special thought as to shape, materials, and finishes. Glass, marble, slate, or plastics, offer not only an endless variety of color and pattern, but are hard, resistant to wear and able to cope with rough usage. Glass, in particular, offers not only a practical working top but affords a sense of spaciousness. When it is used, special emphasis has been placed on the structural beauty of the underneath framework.

Since budgeting of floor area according to its use is part of contemporary architectural thinking, sleeping quarters have become smaller. Modern beds, therefore, have been stripped

George Nelson

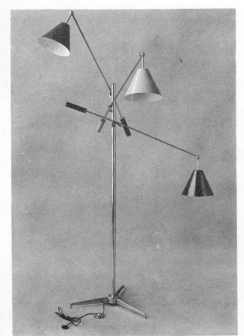

Arredoluce for Raymor

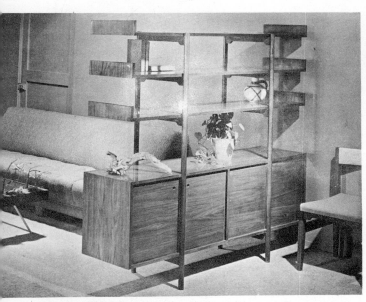

Milo Baughman

T. H. Robsjohn-Gibbings

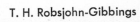

George Nakashima

down to basic essentials, often consisting of nothing more than platform, legs, and mattress. Where headboards are used, they are plain, unadorned and given hard, resistant finishes. The sofa-bed, too, has come into being; one that may be used, without apology, in the living quarters during the day and converted into a guest bed when the occasion arises. This flexibility of arrangement grows steadily more popular as floor space decreases, and points a direction where the bedroom, per se, may become obsolete in the future. The trim, tailored look of modern beds makes them especially welcome in homes where bedrooms often serve as second living rooms for youngsters and teen-agers. Foam rubber, used for mattress or pillows, guarantees, by its quick-recovery qualities a continuously neat, trim appearance.

Lighting fixtures and lamps display the creative genius of leading designers and, like other furnishings, become more and more a part of the architectural overall setup. There is a new flexibility of use, too, in modern lighting; ceiling fixtures may be raised or lowered to meet immediate demands; wall brackets pivot into any desired position. The source of light is always carefully concealed while technological research gives us a soft, even glow with maximum efficiency. Clean lines mark most of the designs, consistent with our demands for open spaciousness. Even table or desk lamps barely seem to touch the surfaces upon which they rest. Materials, usually brass, aluminum, or enameled, are used simply, structurally, and unencumbered with superficial ornament.

Modern fabrics have a new vitality, a new acceptance of synthetic as well as natural materials in their attempt to interpret contemporary living patterns. Plastics, glass, and metal threads add not only new beauty and long wear but make today's fabrics extremely easy to maintain. In the modern home, with its great expanses of glass, fabrics, in many instances, must also substitute as architectural backgrounds, possess texture, whether woven or printed, to compete with the other walls of a room. We find reflections of other creative art forces in their patterns—abstracts, Mondrianesque interrelation of plane and line, stylized natural forms—all contributing a sympathetic understanding of the contem-

Eero Saarinen

Mies van der Rohe

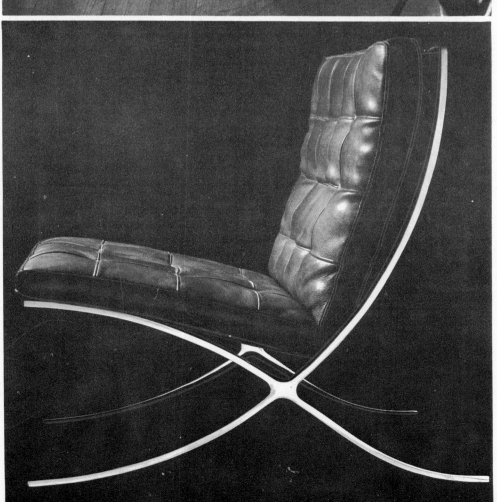

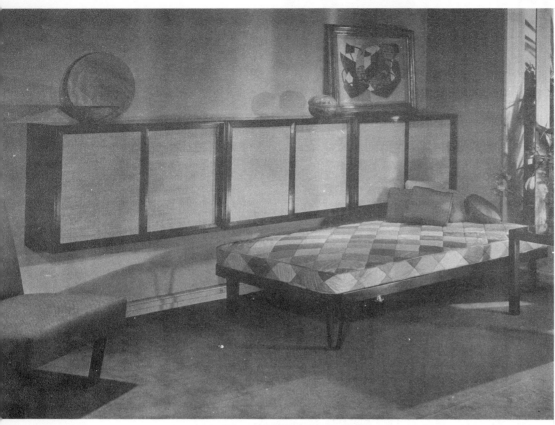

Edward J Wormley

porary scene, all completely in accord with our desire for more representative expression. Color combinations have never been so imaginative and daring and we see a welcome sense of humor, so consistent with our informal living, creeping into many patterns. Weaves are wrinkle-resistant; materials washable. Fast colors and low-cost make them truly representative of the technological advances of a machine-controlled mass-market era.

Modern design as we know it today satisfies a definite need. It has matured sufficiently to be considered an honest, mature style with no apologies to any that has gone before. More and more, it attracts the genius and pioneering abilities of our foremost creative minds in an effort to keep pace with the times, to satisfy the

unique demands of this century. Though we can expect greater development in the future, proper credit should be given to those whose efforts and ingenuity, today, are making homes more comfortable, more efficient, and more attractive places in which to live.

This book is offered as a representative cross section of the best available modern home furnishings. If any worthy examples have been omitted, our humble apologies to both designer and manufacturer. Let me take this opportunity to thank all those who helped me assemble its contents. Let us hope that the results justify their efforts.

WILLIAM J. HENNESSEY

March, 1952

AIRSCHAIRSCHAIRSCHAIRSCHAIRSCHAIRSCHAIRSCHAIRSCHAIRSCHAIRSCHAIRSCHAIRSCHA
AIRSCHAIRSCHAIRSCHAIRSCHAIRSCHAIRSCHAIRSCHAIRSCHAIRSCHAIRSCHAIRSCHAIRSCHA
AIRSCHAIRSCHAIRSCHAIRSCHAIRSCHAIRSCHAIRSCHAIRSCHAIRSCHAIRSCHAIRSCHAIRSCHA
AIRSCHAIRSCHAIRSCHAIRSCHAIRSCHAIRSCHAIRSCHAIRSCHAIRSCHAIRSCHAIRSCHAIRSCHA
AIRSCHAIRSCHAIRSCHAIRSCHAIRSCHAIRSCHAIRSCHAIRSCHAIRSCHAIRSCHAIRSCHAIRSCHA
AIRSCHAIRSCHAIRSCHAIRSCHAIRSCHAIRSCHAIRSCHAIRSCHAIRSCHAIRSCHAIRSCHAIRSCHA
AIRSCHAIRSCHAIRSCHAIRSCHAIRSCHAIRSCHAIRSCHAIRSCHAIRSCHAIRSCHAIRSCHAIRSCHA

No. 108A   Chair
Depth 21"   Width 21"   Height 31"
Material: Walnut with Cane Back
Designer: Tommi Parzinger
For Parzinger Originals, Inc.

Captain's Chair
Depth 26½"   Width 25½"   Height 30"
Material: Walnut or Oak
Designer: William Armbruster
Manufacturer: Edgewood Furniture Co., Inc.

No. 422   Arm Chair
Depth 22"   Width 21"   Height 30½"
Material: Beech with Dark Walnut or Teak Finish

No. 405   Club Table
Length 35½"   Width 35½"   Height 37½"
Material: Reversible Top of Black Felt
   and Walnut or Teak with Matching Beech Legs

Manufacturer: Dux AB Sweden
For Dux Incorporated

No. 5481 "A" Chair
Depth (outside) 26" Width (outside) 21½"
Height 29½"
Material: Laminated Mahogany — One Piece.
Legs — Sheathed in Brass

No. 5474 Table
Diameter 38" Coffee-table Height or up to 28"
Material: Marble top. Mahogany Stem.
Base — Leather Bound in Brass

Designer: Edward J Wormley
Manufacturer: Dunbar Furniture Corporation of Indiana

No. 400½   Chair
Width 27"   Depth 24"   Height 32"
Material: Walnut and Maple or All Walnut

No. 522   Card Table
Length 32"   Width 32"   Height 29"
Material: Walnut Base, Sycamore Top. Also Teakwood

Designer: Finn Juhl
Manufacturer: Baker Furniture, Inc.

No. 71018   Lounge Chair
Depth 26"   Width 24½"   Height 30½"
Material: Walnut
Designers: Kipp Stewart and Stewart MacDougall
Manufacturer: Glenn of California

No. C. 140   Arm Chair
Depth 22½"   Width 22"   Height 32"
Material: Birch or Walnut
Designer: Jens Risom
Manufacturer: Jens Risom Design, Inc.

No. R-24   Arm Chair
Depth 25″   Width 26½″   Height 29½″
Material: Birch. Stained Natural, Walnut or Mahogany
Designers: Edward A. Roffman and M. Lila Neuss
Manufacturer: Edward Axel Roffman Associates, Inc.

No. M-937   Arm Chair
Depth 23″   Width 23″   Height 30½″
Material: Mahogany
Designer: David T. Whitcomb
Manufacturer: Charak Furniture Company

No. 5305   Chair
Depth (outside) 21½"   Width (outside) 26½"
Height 30½"
Material: Mahogany with Brass Stretchers
Designer: Edward J Wormley
Manufacturer: Dunbar Furniture Corporation of Indiana

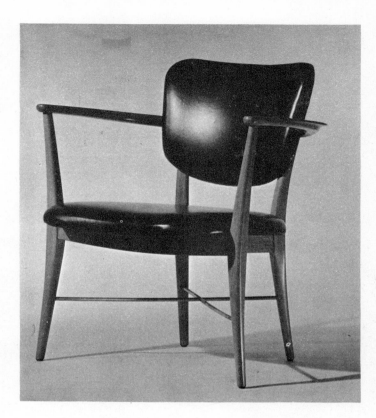

No. 103-83   Arm Chair
Depth 27"   Width 26"   Height 28½"
Material: Elm-stained or Natural Beech
Designer: Arne Hiorth
For George Tanier, Inc.

No. 14-15   Brass Arm Chair
Depth 21"   Width 23"   Height 28"
Material: Finishes — Walnut, Saddle, Nubian Black.
   Brass Arm Rests
Designer: IB Kofod-Larsen
Manufacturer: Selig Manufacturing Company, Inc.

No. 5608   Revolving Dining Chair
Depth 20½"   Width 23½"   Height 27½"
Material: Walnut
Designer: Edward J Wormley
Manufacturer: Dunbar Furniture Corporation of Indiana

No. K84-5   Hoop Chair
Depth 24"   Width 26"   Height 29"
Material: Walnut and Pecan
Designer: John Van Koert
Manufacturer: Drexel Furniture Company

Upper left
No. 433½   Chair
Depth 24"   Width 20½"   Height 31½"
Material: Walnut
Designer: Finn Juhl
Manufacturer: Baker Furniture, Inc.

Upper right
No. 1676   Chair
Depth 18"   Width 19"   Height 33"
Material: Ash, Walnut, Black Lacquer
Designer: Gio Ponti
Manufacturer: Figli di Amedeo
For Altamira

Lower right
No. 416   Arm Chair
Depth 20½"   Width 21"   Height 29"
Material: Beech in Dark Walnut or Teak Finish
Designer: Folke Ohlsson
Manufacturer: Dux AB Sweden
For Dux Incorporated

Upper left
No. 175A   Dining Chair
Depth 21"   Width 17"   Height 34"
Material: Wooden Frame. Finishes — Walnut, Mahogany,
Korina, Cherry, Teak or Rosewood
Designer: Vladimir Kagan
Manufacturer: Kagan-Dreyfuss, Inc.

Lower left
No. 72PSB   Plastic Back Chair
Depth 22"   Width 21"   Height 33"
Material: Plastic Back. Black Oxide or Chrome Finish Base
Designer: Eero Saarinen
Manufacturer: Knoll Associates, Inc.

Lower right
No. 6260   Chair
Depth 21"   Height 35"
Material: Walnut Frame
Designer: Greta Grossman
Manufacturer: Glenn of California

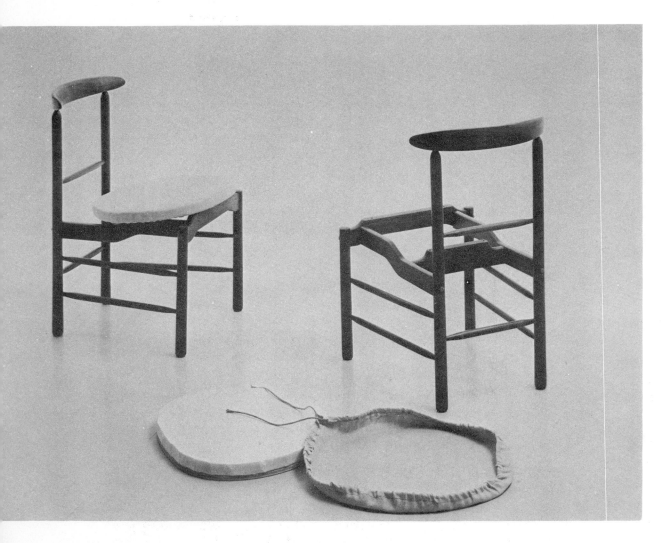

No. 7201   Chair
Depth 21″   Height 35″
Material: Solid Walnut
Designer: Greta Grossman
Manufacturer: Glenn of California

No. 3/LC   Dining Chair
Depth 22"   Width 22"   Height 31½"
Material: Saddle Leather, Chrome-plated
Steel and Black Baked Enamel
Designer and Manufacturer: Laverne Originals

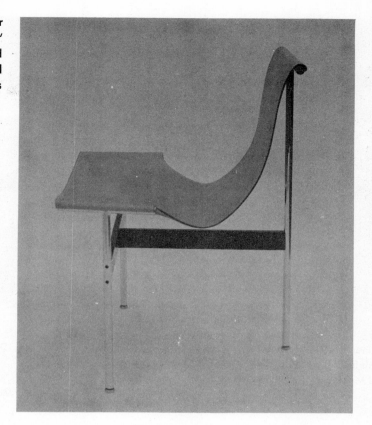

No. OS 6   Chair
Depth 21"   Width 21½"   Height 28"
Material: Beech or Oak
Designer: Helge Bibast
For George Tanier, Inc.

No. WAC 88   Chair
Width 24"   Height 27½"
Material: Walnut or Birch. Rush Seat
Designer and Manufacturer: Smilow-Thielle

Chair
Depth 21½"   Width 23"   Height 32½"
Material: Birch
Designer: Bengt Akerblom
Manufacturer: Nassjo Stolfabrik, Sweden
For Pacific Overseas, Inc.

No. 23   Chair
Depth 16"   Width 16"   Height 30"
Material: Oak with Rush Seat
Designer: Hans J. Wegner
For Bonniers

No. C-200   Chair
Depth 18"   Width 17"   Height 31"
Material: Walnut and Rattan
Designer: Marcel La Riviere
Manufacturer: La Riviere, Inc.
For Ficks Reed Company

Chair
Depth 21¼" Width 19½" Height 32"
Material: Birch
Designer: Bengt Akerblom
Manufacturer: Nassjo Stolfabrik, Sweden
For Pacific Overseas, Inc.

No. 55-75 Chair
Material: Teak Back. Beech Frame
Designer: Finn Juhl
For j g Furniture Company, Inc.

No. FH 4201 Chair
Depth 21" Width 28" Height 30½"
Material: Teak or Walnut. Beech Legs
Designers: Ejner Larsen and A. Bender Madsen
Manufacturer: Fritz Hansens
For George Tanier, Inc.

No. C-201 Chair
Depth (over-all) 20" Width 20" Height 31"
Material: Walnut and Rattan
Designer: Marcel La Riviere
Manufacturer: La Riviere, Inc.
For Ficks Reed Company

No. FH 1935   Loveseat
Depth 26″   Width 51″   Height 27″
Material: Teak or Walnut with Beech Legs
Designer: Hans J. Wegner
For George Tanier, Inc.

Opposite Page
No. 3132   Side Chair
Depth 21″   Width 19″   Height 30″
Material: Rock Maple
Designer: Milo Baughman
Manufacturer: Murray Furniture Manufacturing Company

No. J 48   Side Chair
Depth 20″   Width 19½″   Height 30″
Material: Oak, Oil Finish, or Beech
Designer: Poul M. Volther
For George Tanier, Inc.

No. 7923S   Chair
Depth 19½″   Width 20½″   Height 30½″
Material: Teak and Oxhide
Designers: Ejner Larsen and A. Bender Madsen
Manufacturer: Willy Beck, Denmark
For Pacific Overseas, Inc.

No. 103-84   Arm Chair
Depth 27″   Width 26″   Height 28″
Material: Elm-stained or Natural Birch
Designer: Arne Hiorth
For George Tanier, Inc.

No. 5581   Arm Chair
Depth (outside) 21″   Width (outside) 23″   Height 36½″
Material: Mahogany Frame. Cane Seat
Designer: Edward J Wormley
Manufacturer: Dunbar Furniture Corporation of Indiana

No. 151 Side Chair
Depth 17″ Width 16½″ Height 30″
Material: Maple or Walnut. Cane Seat and Back
Designer: Allan Gould
Manufacturer: Allan Gould Designs, Inc.

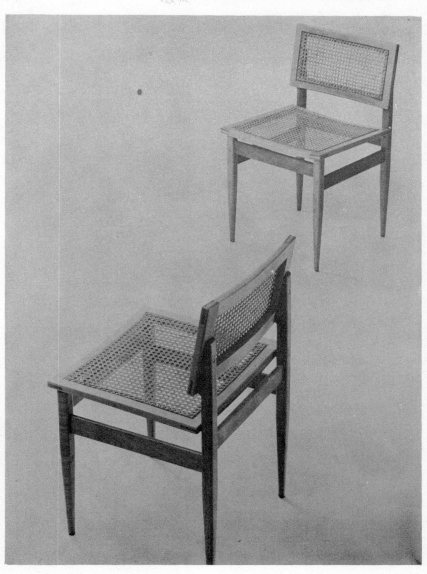

Opposite Page
No. O.S. 52A Arm Chair
Depth 24″ Width 26½″ Height 31″
Material: Teak Frame. Cane Seat and
    Back (or upholstered)
Designer: Arne Vodder
For George Tanier, Inc.

No. 192   Chair
Depth 32"   Width 25½"   Height 30"
Material: Steel Tube Construction. Metalized
    Lacquer Finish
Designer: Darrell Landrum
For Avard

No. 51   Lounge Chair
Depth 31"   Width 24"   Height 30"
Material: Parallel Bar and Rivet Construction.
    Also Solid Teak Base
Designer: Florence Knoll
Manufacturer: Knoll Associates, Inc.

No. 546-5AZ   Chair
Depth 32″   Width 29″   Height 28½″
Material: Cordovan Finish. White Leather Arms
Designer: Norman Fox MacGregor
Manufacturer: Valley Upholstery Corp.

No. 655   Lounge Chair
Depth 24¾″   Width 24¼″   Height 29¼″
Material: Natural Maple Finish Base.
   Contrasting Walnut Panels for Seat
Designer: Lewis Butler
Manufacturer: Knoll Associates, Inc.

No. 5476   Arm Chair
Depth 33"   Width 37"   Height 31"
Material: Walnut or Birch Frame
Designer: George Nelson
Manufacturer: Herman Miller Furniture Company

No. 5482   Chair
Depth (outside) 28"   Width (outside) 22"
  Height 28½"
Material: Mahogany
Designer: Edward J Wormley
Manufacturer: Dunbar Furniture Corporation of Indiana

Chair
Depth 30"   Width 27¼"   Height 29"
Material: Mahogany
Designer: David G. Whitcomb
Manufacturer: Charak Furniture Company

No. U 430   Low Arm Chair
Depth 28″   Width 25″   Height 29″
Material: Birch or Walnut
Designer: Jens Risom
Manufacturer: Jens Risom Design, Inc.

Upper left
No. 378   Chair
Depth 23½"   Width 24"   Height 36"
Material: Walnut Frame
Designer: Robert Balonick
Manufacturer: Marden Mfg. Inc.

Lower left
No. 460 Chair
Depth 28"   Width 24"   Height 31"
Material: Walnut. Oil Finish
Designer: Darrell Landrum
For Avard

Lower right
No. WAC 33   Lounge Chair
Depth 30"   Width 29"   Height 28"
Material: Walnut or Birch
Designer and Manufacturer: Smilow-Thielle

No. 175D   Contour Chair
Depth 37″   Width 33″   Height 37″
Material: Wooden Frame. Finishes—Walnut, Cherry,
Mahogany, Korina, Teak or Rosewood
Designer: Vladimir Kagan
Manufacturer: Kagan-Dreyfuss, Inc.

No. 2024   Chair
Depth 27½"   Width (over-all) 26"   Height 30"

No. 2025   Ottoman
Depth 24"   Width (over-all) 26"   Height 16½"

Material: Walnut Frame Covered in Shell Pink Leather
Designer: T. H. Robsjohn-Gibbings
Manufacturer: The Widdicomb Furniture Company

No. 929   Occasional Chair
Material: Solid Mahogany. "Amber" Finish
Designer: Harvey Probber
Manufacturer: Harvey Probber, Inc.

No. 371   Chair
Depth 33"   Width 27½"   Height 35"
Material: Walnut Frame
Designer: Robert Balonick
Manufacturer: Marden Mfg., Inc.

No. 8505   Chair
Depth 33″   Width 29″   Height 30″
Material: Walnut. Natural Walnut Finish
Designers: Leonard Simmen and Robert Summo
Manuacturer: Erwin-Lambeth, Inc.

No. M S 6   Low Arm Chair
Depth 29½″   Width 26½″   Height 33″
Material: Natural or Walnut-stained Beech,
Lacquer Finish. Teak or Oak, Oil Finish
Designers: A. Bender Madsen and Schubell
For George Tanier, Inc.

No. 63   Lounge Chair
Depth 38"   Width 33"   Height 34"
Material: Swedish Beech. Finishes — Natural,
Teak, Dark Walnut or Black
Designer: Folke Ohlsson
Manufacturer: Dux AB Sweden
For Dux Incorporated

No. 2009 Chair
Depth 29"   Width (over-all) 23½"   Height 31"
Material: Walnut Frame
Designer: T. H. Robsjohn-Gibbings
Manufacturer: The Widdicomb Furniture Company

No. F 47   Easy Chair
Depth 31"   Width 27"   Height 29"
Material: Beech Frame with Walnut Finish
   or Smoked Oak with Teak Arms
Designers. Folke Ohlsson/Alf Svensson
Manufacturer: Dux AB Sweden
For Dux Incorporated

No. 1482   Contour Chair
Depth 36½"   Width (over-all) 26½   Height 36"
Designer: Heritage Design Department
Manufacturer: Heritage Furniture, Inc.

No. 5551   Chair
Depth 33"   Width (over-all) 28"   Height 32"
Material: Solid Walnut. Mocha Finish
Designer and Manufacturer: Furniture by Tomlinson

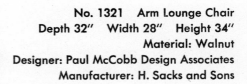

No. 1321   Arm Lounge Chair
Depth 32"   Width 28"   Height 34"
Material: Walnut
Designer: Paul McCobb Design Associates
Manufacturer: H. Sacks and Sons

No. 1750   Occasional Chair
Depth 30"   Width 25½"   Height 30"
Material: Wood Frame. Finishes — Walnut, Korina, Cherry,
   Mahogany, Teak or Rosewood
Designer: Vladimir Kagan
Manufacturer: Kagan-Dreyfuss, Inc.

No. AC-010S   Occasional Settee
Depth 24"   Width 40"   Height 31"
Material: White Ash Frame. Three Standard Oak Finishes
Designer: William Armbruster
Manufacturer: Edgewood Furniture Co., Inc.

No. 56-5　Chair
Depth 30″　Width 27″　Height 31″
Material: Beech with Choice of Finishes
Designer: Arne Vodder
For j g Furniture Company, Inc.

No. C. 108　Arm Chair
Depth 24″　Width 23″　Height 32″
Material: Light Birch or Dark-toned Walnut
Designer: Jens Risom
Manufacturer: Jens Risom Design, Inc.

No. AP 28   Arm Chair
Depth 33"   Width 29"   Height 42"

No. AP 29   Foot Stool
Depth 16"   Width 28"   Height 15"

Material: Teak or Oak
Designer: Hans J. Wegner
For George Tanier, Inc.

No. AP 19   Lounge Chair
Depth 33"   Width 35"   Height 33"
Material: Choice of Danish Woods
Designer: Hans J. Wegner
For George Tanier, Inc.

No. U-453   Low Arm Chair
Depth 31"   Width 30½"   Height 32½"
Material: Birch or Walnut
Designer: Jens Risom
Manufacturer: Jens Risom Design, Inc.

No. 8600   Lounge Chair
Depth 24"   Width (over-all) 30"   Height 48"
Material: Walnut Frame. White Plastic Coasters on Ar
Designers: Kipp Stewart and Stewart MacDougall
Manufacturer: Glenn of California

No. 366   Chair
Depth 33″   Width 27½″   Height 37½″
Material: Walnut Frame
Designer: Robert Balonick
Manufacturer: Marden Mfg., Inc.

No. MEC-701   Hi Back Lounge Chair
Depth 33″   Width 32″   Height 38″
Material: Steel Frame. Foam Rubber Construction
Designer: William Armbruster
Manufacturer: Edgewood Furniture Company, Inc.

No. 361   Chair
Depth 32"   Width 27½"   Height 36"
Material: Walnut Frame
Designer: Homer Tremulis
Manufacturer: Marden Mfg., Inc.

No. 55-92   Lounge Chair and Ottoman
Chair: Depth 32½"   Width 29½"   Height 39½"
Ottoman: Depth 32½"   Width 24"   Height 16"
Material: Teak
Designer: IB Kofod-Larsen
For j g Furniture Company, Inc.

No. SYD-101   Lounger
Depth 35″   Width 35″   Height 40″
Chair has patented mechanical reclining device and
hidden footrest
Designer: Russel Wright
Manufacturer: Sydney Chairs, Inc.

No. 1613   Lounge Chair
Depth (over-all) 32"   Width (over-all) 32"
    Height 27"
Material: Foam Rubber Construction. Brass
    or Solid Walnut Legs
Manufacturer: Furniture by Tomlinson

No. R-5   Chair
Depth 31"   Width 30"   Height 28"
Material: Foam Rubber or Hair Construction
Designers: Edward A. Roffman and M. Lila Neuss
Manufacturer: Edward Axel Roffman Associates, Inc.

No. 580   Chair
Depth 31"   Width 37"
    Height 29"

No. 579   Ottoman
Depth 21"   Width 24"
    Height 16"

Material: Chair — Foam Rubber
    Cushion and Back Padding
Designer and Manufacturer:
    Selig Mfg. Co., Inc.

Upper left
No. R-18   Hi-Back Club Chair
Depth 31"   Width 28"   Height 34½"
Material: Legs of Natural Birch, Stained Walnut
or Mahogany. Rubberized Hair,
Latex Foam Rubber Construction
Designers: Edward A. Roffman and M. Lila Neuss
Manufacturer: Edward Axel Roffman
Associates, Inc.

Lower left
No. 155   Chair
Depth 31"   Width 31"   Height 30"
Material: Brass Legs. Reversible Cushion
Designer: Carlo De Carli
Manufacturer: M. Singer & Sons

Lower right
No. 954   Arm Chair
Depth 33"   Width 34"
Height 30"
Material: Foam Rubber Seat
and Back Cushion
Designer and Manufacturer:
Selig Mfg. Co., Inc.

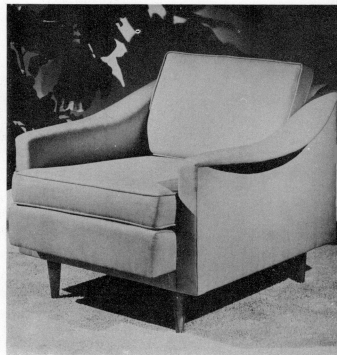

No. 915   Pull-up Chair
Material: Mahogany. "Resin" Finish. Cane Back.
Designer: Harvey Probber
Manufacturer: Harvey Probber, Inc.

No. 310-A   Arm Chair
Depth 32"   Width 24"   Height 27"
Material: Ebony or Walnut Frame. Cane Arms and Back
Designer: Paul Colby
Manufacturer: Colby Associates

No. 367   Chair
Depth 31½″   Width 24½″   Height 32″
Material: Walnut Frame. Rubber Seat and Reversible
Rubber Back Pillow
Designer: Dick Tremulis
Manufacturer: Marden Mfg., Inc.

No. 5480   Chair
Depth (over-all) 25″   Width (over-all) 24½″   Height 33″
Material: Laminated Ash Frame with Brass Feet. Cane Back
Designer: Edward J Wormley
Manufacturer: Dunbar Furniture Corporation of Indiana

No. 670   Lounge Chair
Depth (over-all) 32"   Width (over-all) 33"   Height 33½"
Material: Molded Rosewood Plywood Shell. Interchangeable
   Cushions of Feather, Down over Foam Rubber.
   Cushions — Black Leather, Fabric or Naugahyde
Designer: Charles Eames
Manufacturer: Herman Miller Furniture Company

No. 180B   Contour Chair
Depth 26″   Width 41″   Height 39″
Material: Stainless Steel. Wooden Hand Rests Covered
in Natural Cowhide or in Fabric
Designer: Vladimir Kagan
Manufacturer: Kagan-Dreyfuss, Inc.

Upper left
No. 3136   Wood Scoop Chair
Depth 26"   Width 24"   Height 30½"
Material: Rock Maple. Natural Saddle Leather
Designer: Milo Baughman
Manufacturer: Murray Furniture Manufacturing Company

Upper right
No. 688-2AZ   Occasional Chair
Depth 29½"   Width 29½"   Height 29"
Material: Wood Base. Walnut Finish. Leather Seat and Back
Designer: Norman Fox MacGregor
Manufacturer: Valley Upholstery Corporation

Lower left
No. 6001   Executive Chair
Depth 27"   Width 23"   Height 37"
Material: Cast Aluminum Base. Leather Upholstery
Designer: Paul McCobb Design Associates
Manufacturer: H. Sacks & Sons

No. 175E   Contour Chair
Depth 32"   Width 29"   Height 32"
Material: Wooden Frame. Finishes — Walnut, Mahogany,
    Cherry, Korina, Teak or Rosewood. Natural Cowhide Seat
Designer: Vladimir Kagan
Manufacturer: Kagan-Dreyfuss, Inc.

No. 1751   Contour Chair
Depth 33"   Width 20"   Height 29"
Material: Wooden Legs. Finishes — Walnut, Cherry,
    Mahogany, Korina, Teak, Rosewood. Black Leather Seat
Designer: Vladimir Kagan
Manufacturer: Kagan-Dreyfuss, Inc.

No. 5569   Coconut Chair
Depth 33"   Width 40"   Height 32½"
Material: Chromium-plated Steel Base. Foam Rubber on
    Flat Sheet Steel for Seat and Back
Designer: George Nelson
Manufacturer: Herman Miller Furniture Company

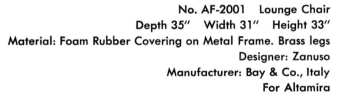

No. AF-2001   Lounge Chair
Depth 35"   Width 31"   Height 33"
Material: Foam Rubber Covering on Metal Frame. Brass legs
Designer: Zanuso
Manufacturer: Bay & Co., Italy
For Altamira

No. 55-64   Chair
Depth 19½"   Width 17½"   Height 30"
Material: Black or White Molded Fiberglas,
    Polished Steel Frame
Designer: I. B. Kofod-Larsen
For j g Furniture Co., Inc.

No. 405   Sculptured Chair
Seat Height 14" or 17"
Material: Wrought Iron with Woven Wire
Designer and Manufacturer: Lee L. Woodard Sons

No. DAT — 1   Plastic Shell Chair
Depth 23"   Width 24⅞"   Height 34"
Seat Height from 16" to 20"
Material: Plastic with or without Foam Rubber Upholstery
Designer: Charles Eames
Manufacturer: Herman Miller Furniture Company

No. 356   Brass Arm Chair
Depth 24"   Width 22"   Height 34"
Material: Brass. Brushed Brass Finish
Designer: Vladimír Kagan
Manufacturer: Kagan-Dreyfuss, Inc.

No. 357   Brass Side Chair
Depth 24"   Width 15"   Height 34"
Material: Brass. Brushed Brass Finish
Designer: Vladimír Kagan
Manufacturer: Kagan-Dreyfuss, Inc.

No. 2201   Arm Chair
Depth 24"   Width 20½"   Height 27"

No. 2209   Ottoman
Depth 23"   Width 24"   Height 14½"

Material: Structural Black Metal Frame of Tubular Steel
    (in round or square tubing). Vertical Suspension Rods
    of 1-inch Solid Brass. Seats and Back of Foam Rubber
Designer: Don Knorr
Manufacturer: Vista Furniture Company

No. 865   Hi-Back Club Chair
Depth 22"   Width 21"   Height 40"
Material: Hand-woven Rattan and Metal
Designers: Hendrik Van Keppel
   and Taylor Green
Manufacturer: Van Keppel-Green

No. 210 Love Seat
Depth 17" Width 42½" Height (over-all) 28½"
Material: Black Steel, Natural Rush with Birch or Walnut
Designer: Arthur Umanoff
For Raymor

Upper left
No. 211   Lounge Chair
Depth 16¾"   Width 23½"   Height 27¾"
Material: Black Steel, Natural Rush
   and Hardwood.
   Birch or Walnut Finish Seat
Designer: Arthur Umanoff
For Raymor

Upper right
No. 3133   Fibre Chair
Depth 22"   Width 17½"   Height 30"
Material: Rock Maple and Fibre
Designer: Milo Baughman
Manufacturer: Murray Furniture
   Manufacturing Company

Lower right
No. 103   Bow Chair
Depth 19"   Width 20"   Height 29"
Material: Cotton Yacht Cord or Braided
   Plastic Cord. Black Steel Frame
Designer: Allan Gould
Manufacturer: Allan Gould Designs, Inc.

Upper left
No. 206   Chair
Depth 14″   Width 16½″   Height 32″
Material: Maple Wood Slat Seat. Woven Rush Back.
Wrought Iron Frame
Designer: Arthur Umanoff
For Raymor

Lower left
No. 101   Chair
Depth 15″   Width 17″   Height 33″
Material: Hardwood and Black Iron
Designer: Arthur Umanoff
For Raymor

Lower right
No. 202   Chair
Depth 15″   Width 17¼″   Height 31″
Material: Natural Birch or Walnut-finish Seat.
Hand-woven and Lacquered Reed Back. Black Iron Frame
Designer: Arthur Umanoff
For Raymor

No. 5641   Bar Stool
Depth 20½"   Width 21"   Height 37"
Material: Walnut with Brass Stretchers.
   Laminated Toprail and Slats
Designer: Edward J Wormley
Manufacturer: Dunbar Furniture Corporation of Indiana

No. 5570   Dressing Table Bench
Depth (ouside) 15"   Width 23"   Height 21½"
Material: Mahogany and Leather
Designer: Edward J Wormley
Manufacturer: Dunbar Furniture Corporation of Indiana

No. 510   Bench
Length 23"   Width 15"   Height 17"
Material: Wood and Hand-made Rush Seat.
Finishes — Walnut, Mahogany, Cherry,
Korina, Teak or Rosewood
Designer: Vladimir Kagan
Manufacturer: Kagan-Dreyfuss, Inc.

No. 5002   Bench
Length 23"   Width 23"
Height 17"
Material: Mahogany Turned
Legs and Stretchers.
Buttoned Rubber Seat
Designer: Edward J Wormley
Manufacturer: Dunbar
Furniture Corporation
of Indiana

No. 85T   Rocking Stool (left)
Diameter 14"   Height 10½"

No. 86T   Rocking Stool (right)
Diameter 14"   Height 16¾"

Material: Tops — Solid Teak or Walnut with Natural
    Waxed Finishes. Chrome Finished V-shaped Steel Rods
Designer: Isamu Noguchi
Manufacturer: Knoll Associates, Inc.

No. 104   Bow Stool
Depth 18"   Width 20"   Height 15"
Material: Cotton Yacht Cord or Braided Plastic Cord.
Black Steel Frame
Designer: Allan Gould
Manufacturer: Allan Gould Design, Inc.

Donut Stools
Diameter 15"   Height 18"
Material: Steel Legs. Fabric
    or Leather Top.
    Rubberized Hair Filling
Designer: William Armbruster
Manufacturer: Edgewood Furniture
    Company, Inc.

No. 120   Stool
Depth 24"   Width 24"   Height 17"
Material: Steel Structure Finished Black.
    Foam Rubber Cushion
Designer: Darrell Landrum
For Avard

No. 3130   Folding Seat
Depth 15"   Width 18"   Height 15"
Material: Leather Seat with Brass Rivets
Designer: Milo Baughman
Manufacturer: Murray Furniture
    Manufacturing Company

No. 1306   Brass All Around Square
Depth 20"   Width 20"   Height 16"
Material: Brass with White
    Naugahyde Seat
Designer: Paul McCobb Design
    Associates
Manufacturer: Directional
    Manufacturing Co.

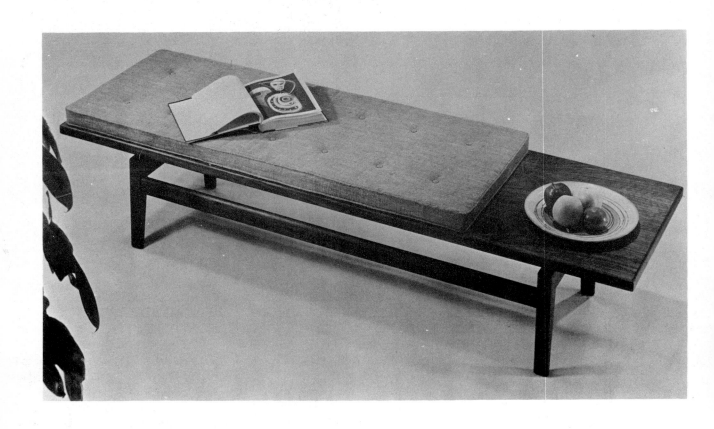

No. T.621   Low Table
Length 72″   Width 21″   Height 15″
Material: Birch or Walnut
Designer: Jens Risom
Manufacturer: Jens Risom Design, Inc.

No. 5   Bench
Length 48"   Depth 22"   Height 23"
Material: Magnesium Frame and Foam Rubber Seat
Designer and Manufacturer: Dwight Furniture Company

No. 11C   Bench
Length 74"   Width 26½"   Height 14"
Material: Natural Saddle Leather. Chrome Plated
    Steel Angle Legs
Designer and Manufacturer: Laverne Originals

BLESTABLESTABLESTABLESTABLESTABLESTABLESTABLESTABLESTABLESTABLES**TABLES**TABLESTABLEST
BLESTABLESTABLESTABLESTABLESTABLESTABLESTABLESTABLESTABLESTABLES**TABLES**TABLESTABLEST
BLESTABLESTABLESTABLESTABLESTABLESTABLESTABLESTABLESTABLESTABLES**TABLES**TABLESTABLEST
BLESTABLESTABLESTABLESTABLESTABLESTABLESTABLESTABLESTABLESTABLES**TABLES**TABLESTABLEST
BLESTABLESTABLESTABLESTABLESTABLESTABLESTABLESTABLESTABLESTABLES**TABLES**TABLESTABLEST
BLESTABLESTABLESTABLESTABLESTABLESTABLESTABLESTABLESTABLESTABLES**TABLES**TABLESTABLEST
BLESTABLESTABLESTABLESTABLESTABLESTABLESTABLESTABLESTABLESTABLES**TABLES**TABLESTABLES

No. 220   Table
Length 56"   Width 28"   Height 28"
Material: Oil Finish Teak Top. Metalized Steel Base

No. 135   Dining Chair
Depth 16"   Height 33"
Material: Metalized Steel Structure

Designer: Darrell Landrum
For Avard

Table
Length 71"   Width 35½"   Height 28"
Material: Teak and Oak. Natural Finish.
Brass Understructure

Chairs
Depth 19¼"   Height 30"
Material: Teak and Oak. Natural Finish.
Woven Sea Grass Seat

Designer: Borge Mogensen
Manufacturer: Soborg Mobelfabrik
For Pacific Overseas, Inc.

No. 5493   Flip-Flop Tables
Length 54″   Width (closed) 18″   (open) 36″   Height 29″
Material: Tawi Wood Tops. Mahogany Base with Brass Shoes

No. 5480   Chairs
Depth (outside) 25″   Width (outside) 24½″ Height 33″
Material: Laminated Ash Frame with Brass Feet

Designer: Edward J Wormley
Manufacturer: Dunbar Furniture Corporation of Indiana

No. 10/T   Dining Table
Length 84"   Width 36"   Height 27"
Material: Teak or Marble with Chrome Plated or
    Brass Steel Legs
Designer and Manufacturer: Laverne Originals

No. 417   Drop-Leaf Dining Table
Length 66"   Width (closed) 19"   (open) 42"   Height 29½"
Material: Finishes — Walnut, Mahogany, Cherry, Korina,
Rosewood or Teak
Designer: Vladimir Kagan
Manufacturer: Kagan-Dreyfuss, Inc.

No. 5558   Extension Dining Table with
   Separate Leaf Extension
Length (closed) 72″   (open) 112″   Width 40″
Material: Walnut

No. 5468   Chairs
Depth 21¼″   Width 19″   Height 31¾″
Material: Birch Frames. Walnut Backs

Designer: George Nelson
Manufacturer: Herman Miller Furniture Company

No. 220　Table
Length 60"　Width 30"　Height 28"
Material: Realwood Walnut Formica Top.
Steel Construction. Finished Black

No. 223　Chairs
Depth 19½"　Width 19"　Height 29½"
Material: Walnut. Natural Oil Finish.
Steel Construction. Finished Black

Designer: Darrell Landrum
For Avard

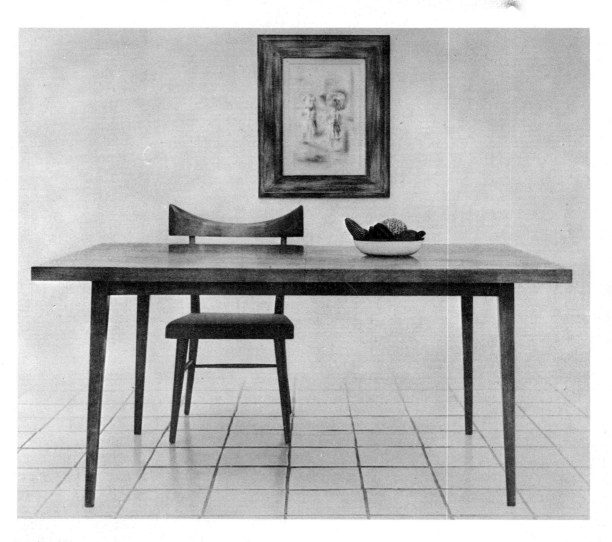

No. 1528   Dining Table
No. 1528-P   Dining Table W/Plastic Top
Length (closed) 60"   (open) 84"   Width 36"
Material: Finishes — Natural, Tobacco, Black, Walnut
Designer: Paul McCobb Design Associates
Manufacturer: Winchendon Furniture Company

No. 200   Compass Table
Length 60"   Width 32"
    Height 28½"
Material: Walnut or Maple
Designer: Allan Gould
Manufacturer: Allan Gould
    Designs, Inc.

No. 202W   Extension Table
Width 48"   Height 28½"   Depth 32" to 48"
Material: Plastic or Wood Top. Solid Wood Base
Designer: Allan Gould
Manufacturer: Allan Gould Designs, Inc.

No. 1634   Double Top Console Dinette Table
Length 54"   Width (closed) 20"   (open) 40"   Height 30¾"
Material: Oak. Colors — Acorn, Weathered Platinum,
    Charcoal, Natural Oak
Designer: Herbert Ten Have
Manufacturer: Sligh Furniture

No. 205   Table
Length 78"   Width 24"   Height 27"
Material: Steel Structure. Finished Black.
White Formica Top
Designer: Darrell Landrum
For Avard

No. 410XT   Convertible Table
Length 36″   Depth (closed) 20″   (open) 40″
    Height 30″
Material: Walnut, Birch or Ebony Finish.
    White Micarta Top on Inside
Designer: Paul Colby
Manufacturer: Colby Associates

No. 500½   Library Table
Length 78″   Width 37″   Height 28½″
Material: Walnut Base. Sycamore Top
Designer: Finn Juhl
Manufacturer: Baker Furniture, Inc.

| | No. 4301 | Dining Table |
| Length 68″ (extends to 104″)   Width 40″ | Height 29″ | 2-18″ Leaves |

| | No. 4309 | Dining Table |
| Length 58″ (extends to 78″)   Width 38″ | Height 29″ | 1-20″ Leaf |

| | No. 4206 | Arm Chair |
| Depth 27½″   Width 23¼″ | Height 35″ | |

| | No. 4206 | Side Chair |
| Depth 27½″   Width 22¼″ | Height 35″ | |

Material: Walnut
Designer: T. H. Robsjohn-Gibbings
Manufacturer: The Widdicomb Furniture Company

No. 4147   Dining Extension Table
Length (closed) 60″   (open) 84″   Width 36″   Height 29″
Material: Rock Maple
Designer: Milo Baughman
Manufacturer: Murray Furniture Manufacturing Company

No. M-1155   Table
Length 65"   Width 45"   (open) 10'   Height 29"
Material: Quartered Teak Veneer. Natural or
   Dark Wax Finish. Legs Solid Walnut

No. M-1158   Chairs
Material: Solid Walnut

Designer: Harold M. Schwartz
Manufacturer: Romweber

No. 5575   Round-Square Table
Length (closed) 38″   (open) 54″   Width 38″   Height 29″
Material: Mahogany
Designer: Edward J Wormley
Manufacturer: Dunbar Furniture Corporation of Indiana

No. 4307   Dining Table
Length 76″   (and extended 118″)   Width 44″
Three 14″ leaves   Height 28¾″

No. 4207   Arm Chair
Depth 22″   Width 23½″   Height 34″

No. 4207   Side Chair
Depth 21¾″   Width 23″   Height 34″

Material: Walnut. Finishes — Sorrel, Sienna, Sherry,
Saffron or Cordovan
Designer: T. H. Robsjohn-Gibbings
Manufacturer: The Widdicomb Furniture Company

No. 423   Drop-leaf Dining Table
Length 42″   Width (closed) 18″
(open) 66″   Height 28½″
Material: Finishes — Walnut,
Mahogany, Cherry, Korina,
Rosewood or Teak
Designer: Vladimir Kagan
Manufacturer: Kagan-Dreyfuss, Inc.

No. 3603   Table
Length 45½″   Width 33½″
Height 27½″

No. 3100   Chair
Depth 19″   Width 16¼″
Height 30¼″

Material: Beech — Stained Black,
Oak, Teak, Beech,
Walnut or Palisander
Designer: Arne Jacobsen
Manufacturer: Fritz Hansens
For Pacific Overseas, Inc.

No. 7102   Drop-leaf Table
Length 60"   Width (closed) 18"
    (open) 54"   Height 28½"
Material: Solid Walnut with
    Ebonized Tips
Designer: Greta Grossman
Manufacturer: Glenn of California

No. T-181   "Squared Circle" Table
Length 48" (can be extended
    by 3-16" leaves to 96")
Width 48"   Height 29"
Material: Birch or Walnut
Designer: Jens Risom
Manufacturer: Jens Risom Design, Inc.

No. 3143   Round Extension Dining Table
Length (closed) 48″   (open) 72″
Width 48″   Height 29″
Material: Rock Maple
Designer: Milo Baughman
Manufacturer: Murray Furniture
Manufacturing Company

No. 7103   Dining Table
Length 45″   Width 45″
Height 28½″
Material: Walnut
Designer: Greta Grossman
Manufacturer: Glenn of California

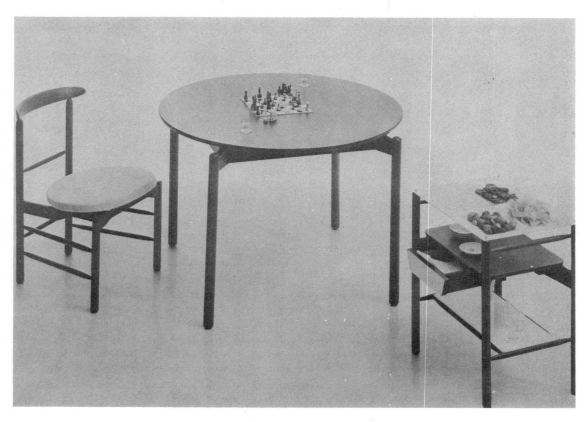

No. 4313   Dining Table
Length 60"   Width 60"   Height 30½"

No. 4212   Side Chair
Depth 19"   Width 24"   Height 33½"

Material: Walnut. Finishes — Sorrel, Sherry or Sienna
Designer: T. H. Robsjohn-Gibbings
Manufacturer: The Widdicomb Furniture Company

No. T332   Low Table
Length 32"   Width 32"   Height 16"
Material: Birch or Walnut
Designer: Jens Risom
Manufacturer: Jens Risom Design, Inc.

No. 39T   Coffee Table
Length 37½"   Depth 36"
    Height 16½"
Material: Walnut. Wood, Formica
    or Marble Top
    in Six Variations
Designer: Dick Tremulis
Manufacturer: Marden Mfg., Inc.

No. 2253   Lamp Table
Length 28"   Width 24"   Height 20"
Material: Mahogany Frame. Plastic
or Wood Top
Designer: Don Knorr
Manufacturer: Vista Furniture Company

No. 38T   Table
Length 28"   Depth 38"   Height 16"
Material: Brass Construction. Wood
or Formica Top
Designer: Robert Balonick
Manufacturer: Marden Mfg., Inc.

No. 3322   Table
Length 32"   Width 32"   Height 22"
Material: Walnut
Designer: T. H. Robsjohn-Gibbings
Manufacturer: The Widdicomb
Furniture Company

No. 22-T   Coffee Table
Length 68"   Depth 18"   Height 15"
Material: Walnut. Top with Formica Insert in Solid Colors
Designer: Robert Balonick
Manufacturer: Marden Mfg., Inc.

No. 6405   Free Form Cocktail Table
Length 60″   Width 48″   Height 15″
Material: Walnut
Designer: Greta Grossman
Manufacturer: Glenn of California

No. 35T   Table
Length 72"   Depth 17½"   Height 16"
Material: Walnut
Designer: Homer Tremulis
Manufacturer: Marden Mfg., Inc.

No. 51018   Cocktail Table
Length 62"   Width 24"   Height 14"
Material: Walnut. "Marba-Rok" Top. Walnut Base
Designers: Kipp Stewart and Stewart MacDougall
Manufacturer: Glenn of California

No. 3175   Surf Board Cocktail Table
Length 66"   Width 21"   Height 14½"
Material: Rock Maple
Designer: Milo Baughman
Manufacturer: Murray Furniture Manufacturing Company

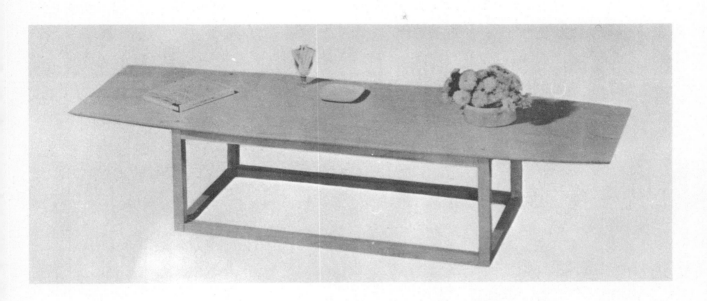

No. 51048   Free Form Cocktail Table
Material: Walnut Veneer Top. Solid Walnut Base
Designers: Kipp Stewart and Stewart MacDougall
Manufacturer: Glenn of California

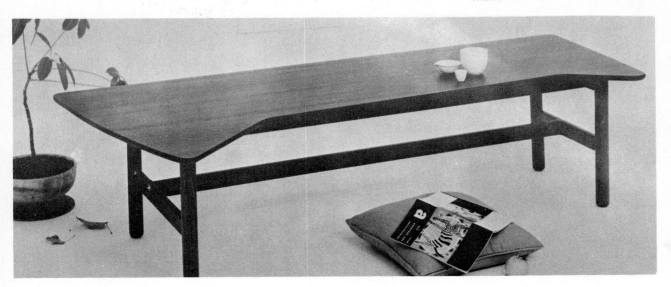

115

No. 320-C   Cocktail Table
Material: Shell

No. 310-C   Cocktail Table
Material: Natural Walnut

Length 66″   Width 17½″   Height 14½″
Designer: Heritage Design Department
Manufacturer: Heritage Furniture, Inc.

No. 6401   Free Form Cocktail Table
Length 60″   Width 36″   Height 14½″
Material: Stump Walnut, Light or Dark. Brass Base
Designer: Greta Grossman
Manufacturer: Glenn of California

No. 3356   Cocktail Table
Diameter 48″   Height 15″
Material: Walnut. Finishes — Sorrel,
Sherry, Sienna
Designer: T. H. Robsjohn-Gibbings
Manufacturer: The Widdicomb
Furniture Company

118

No. 352 Table
Diameter 54" Height 25½"
Material: Maple on Walnut Legs. Also Walnut
Plywood Surface and Base of Laminated Maple
Stretchers and Legs
Designer: Lewis Butler
Manufacturer: Knoll Associates, Inc.

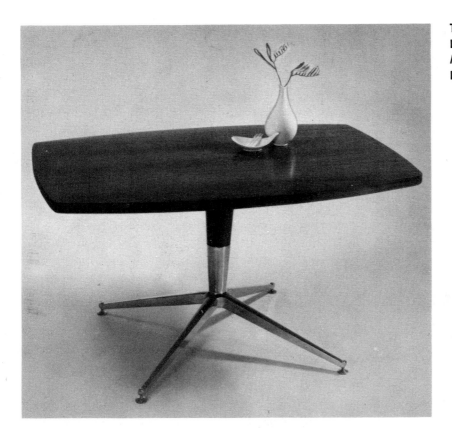

Table
Length 42″   Depth 28″   Height 22″
Material: Brass Base. Walnut and Formica Top
Danish Design for j g Furniture Company, Inc.

No. 899   Hexagonal Cocktail Table
Diameter 42″
Material: "Stone-Brass" Top with Solid
    Brass Inlay. Solid Mahogany Base
Designer: Harvey Probber
Manufacturer: Harvey Probber, Inc.

No. 307-C   Cocktail Table
Material: Natural Walnut with Slate Top

No. 317-C   Cocktail Table
Material: Shell Finish with Slate Top

Diameter 40"   Height 16"
Designer: Heritage Design Department
Manufacturer: Heritage Furniture, Inc.

No. 172   Cocktail Table
Diameter 40"   Height 14½"
Material: White Marble Top. Red Lacquered
Base. Brass Feet
Designer: Tommi Parzinger
For Parzinger Originals, Inc.

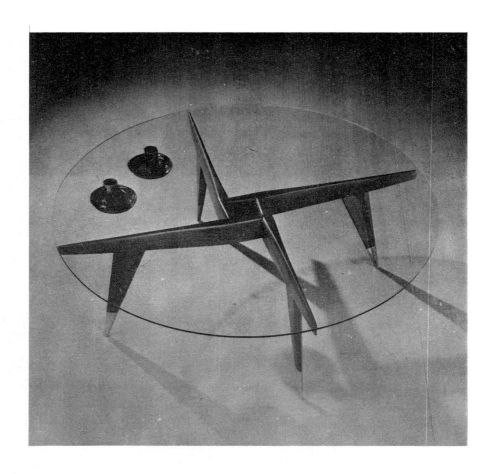

No. 2155   Table
Diameter 41¼"   Height 14¼"
Material: Solid Walnut Legs. Brass Feet.
   Tempered Demi-Plate Glass Top
Designer: Gio Ponti
Manufacturer: M. Singer & Sons

No. 1128   Table
Diameter 27"   Height 17¼"
Material: Solid Brass Supports.
   Removable One-half-inch Plate Glass
Designer: Singer Design Staff
Manuacturer: M. Singer & Sons

No. 60L   Swastika Base Cocktail Table
Material: Rawhide Bindings. Glass Top

No. 60R   Swastika Base Cocktail Table
Material: Reed Bindings. Glass Top

Diameter 42"   Height 15½"
Designer: Eleanor Forbes
Manufacturer: The McGuire Company

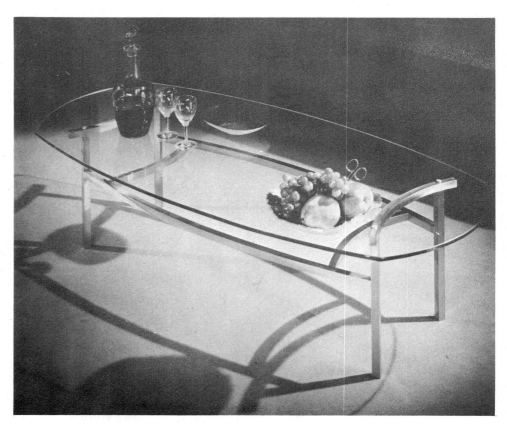

No. 1124   Cocktail Table
Length 52"   Width 12"   Height 14"
Material: Glass Top. Brass Base
Designer: Bertha Schaefer
Manufacturer: M. Singer & Sons

No. 5309   Cocktail Table
Length 57½"   Width 31"   Height 16½"
Material: Rosewood Legs with Solid Cast Polished
    Brass Stretcher. Half-inch Plate Glass Top
Designer: Edward J Wormley
Manufacturer: Dunbar Furniture
    Corporation of Indiana

No. E5522   Cocktail Table
Width (over-all) 34"   Glass Diameter 31½"
    Height 17½"
Material: Iron Frame. Glass Top. Italian Wicker Basket
Designer: Maurizio Tempestini
Manufacturer: John B. Salterini Co., Inc.

No. T390   Low Table
Length 52"   Width 24"   Height 17"
Material: Birch or Walnut
Designer: Jens Risom
Manufacturer: Jens Risom Design, Inc.

No. 5404   Interlocking Tables

No. 5402   Zebra Wood with White Micarta Top and Shelf
Length 86"   Width 15½"   Height 15"

No. 5403   Zebra Wood
Length 53½"   Width 23"   Height 24"

Designer: Edward J Wormley
Manuacturer: Dunbar Furniture Corporation of Indiana

No. 5631   Cocktail Table
Top (upper) 33½" x 21"   (lower) 14½" x 21"
Length (over-all) 54"   Height 14½"
Material: Upper Top — Figured Cherry Veneer Banded in
Solid Mahogany. Lower top — Figured Mahogany Veneer.
Underparts — Solid Mahogany. Brass Ferrules, Magazine
Basket and Trim Strips
Designer: J. Gordon Perlmutter
Manufacturer: The Brandt Cabinet Works Inc.

No. 2169   Table "Holiday"
Length 60"   Width 24"   Height 14"
Material: Cherry and Teak
Designer: Lorin Jackson
Manufacturer: Imperial Furniture Company

No. 57L   Nest of Three Tables
Length (large table) 51"   Width 22"   Height 16½"
Material: Rattan with Rawhide Bindings. White Micarta Top

No. 56L   Small Table
Length 25½"   Width 17"   Height 13"
Material: Rattan with Rawhide Bindings. Philippine Mahogany Top

Designer: Eleanor Forbes
Manuacturer: The McGuire Company

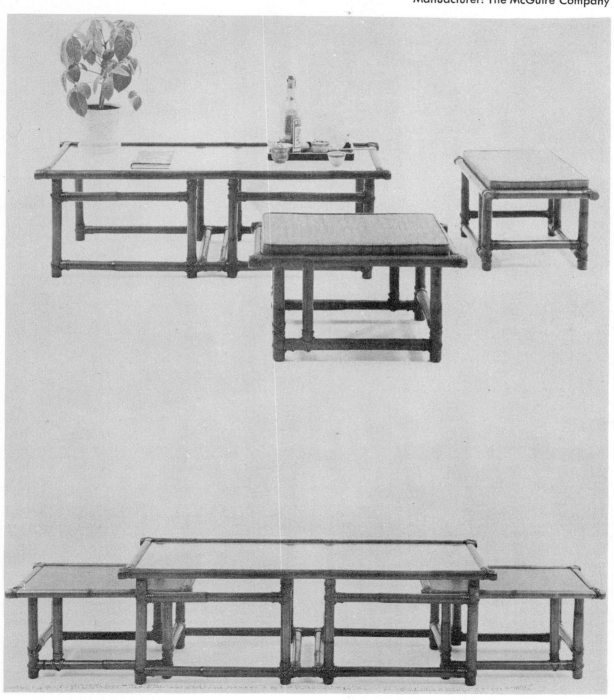

No. T-2   Table
Length 42″   Width 17″   Height 16″
Material: Walnut and Brass
Designer: Ernest Lowy
Manufacturers: Koch & Lowy Mfg. Co.

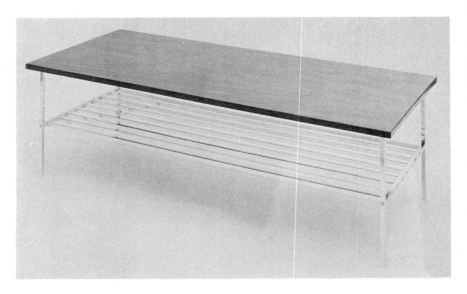

No. 2251   Coffee Table
Length 52½″   Width 24″   Height 12″
Material: Wood Frame. Plastic or Wood Top
Designer: Don Knorr
Manufacturer: Vista Furniture Company

No. 431-16   Table
Length 48"   Width 31"   Height 16"
Material: Rectangular Steel Tubing Frame. Redwood Top
Designers: Hendrik Van Keppel and Taylor Green
Manufacturer: Van Keppel-Green

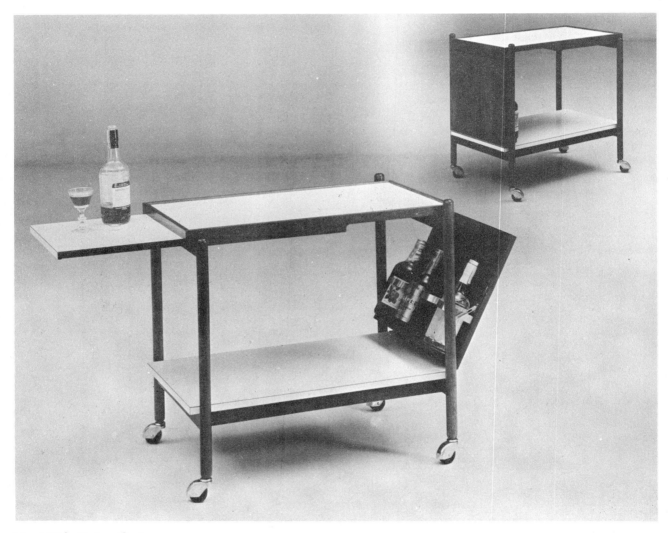

No. 6413   Hostess Cart
Length 32″   Width 30″   Height 18″
Material: Solid Walnut Frame. White Formica Shelves
Designer: Greta Grossman
Manufacturer: Glenn of California

No. TW-9   Tea Wagon
Length 36″   Width 18″   Height 24″
Material: Walnut or Birch. Formica Top Optional
Designer and Manufacturer: Smilow-Thielle

No. BJ 1604   Drop-leaf Cart
Length (open) 62″ (leaves dropped) 38″
Width 19″   Height 30″
Material: Formica Top. Walnut Drawer.
   Plate Glass Shelf.
   Solid Brass Frame
Designer: George Mergenov
For Raymor

No. 5433   Party Server
Length (closed) 26¾″   (open) 53½″
Depth 21½″   Height 31½″
Material: Walnut with Black Formica Top.
Japanese Pine Panelling Doors
Designer: Edward J Wormley
Manufacturer: Dunbar Furniture
Corporation of Indiana

No. 5433   Party Server Closed

No. 5534   Single Drawer Dressing Table or Desk
Width 32"   Depth 18"   Height 29½"
Material: Figured White Cherry. Brass and
White Cherry Pedestals

No. 5522   Swivel Chair
Seat Diameter 18"   Height 29½"
Material: Cane Posture Back

Designer: Edward J Wormley
Manufacturer: Dunbar Furniture Corporation of Indiana

No. 5345   Reading or Solitaire Table
Length 44½"   Width 15"   Height 26½"
Material: Mahogany. Charal (Nut Brown) Finish
Designer: Warner R. Cleveland
Manufacturer: Imperial Furniture Company

No. 952   Portable Bar
Material: Mahogany in Variety of Finishes.
Beige Carrara Top
Designer: Harvey Probber
Manufacturer: Harvey Probber, Inc.

No. 5311   Drop-leaf Table
Length (closed) 20″   (open) 38″   Depth 28″   Height 26″
Material: Walnut Top. Mahogany Case Suspended
Designer: Edward J Wormley
Manufacturer: Dunbar Furniture Corporation of Indiana

Table Open

No. 953   Utility Side Table
Material: Mahogany. "Resin" and Other Finishes
Designer: Harvey Probber
Manufacturer: Harvey Probber, Inc.

No. 52048   End Table
Length 20″   Width 20″   Height 24″
Material: Walnut Veneer Top and Drawer Unit.
Solid Walnut Base
Designers: Kipp Stewart and Stewart MacDougall
Manufacturer: Glenn of California

No. 5645   Chairside Table
Length 30"   Width 20"   Height 24½"
Material: Figured Cherry Veneered Top Banded in
   Solid Mahogany. Figured Mahogany Sides, Drawer
   Front and Shelf. Solid Mahogany Legs. Brass
   End Rods and Ferrules
Designer: J. Gordon Perlmutter
Manufacturer: The Brandt Cabinet Works, Inc.

No. 3103   Storage Table
Length 24″   Width 24″   Height 21″
Material: Rock Maple
Designer: Milo Baughman
Manufacturer: Murray Furniture Manufacturing Company

No. 52028   End Table
Length 26″   Width 20″   Height 23″
Material: Walnut
Designers: Kipp Stewart and Stewart MacDougall
Manufacturer: Glenn of California

No. T.408   End Table
Length 30"   Width 21"   Height 22"
Material: Birch or Walnut
Designer: Jens Risom
Manufacturer: Jens Risom Design, Inc.

Server or Utility Table
Length 36"   Width 20"   Height 30"
Material: Walnut
Designer and Manufacturer: Charles Pechanec, Jr.

No. 175   Console Table
Length 48″   Width 14″   Height 31″
Material: Steel Structure. Metallized Lacquer
    Finish. Teak Top
Designer: Darrell Landrum
For Avard

Nesting Tables
Length 24"   Width 16"   Height 18"
Length 18"   Width 16"   Height 17½"
Length 12"   Width 16"   Height 16½"
Material: Oak with Walnut-tipped Legs
(Colored) Marba-Rok Tops
Designer and Manufacturer: Charles Pechanec, Jr.

No. 402   Nest of Tables
Length 28"   Width 16"   Height 20"
Material: Wood Base. Finishes—Walnut, Korina,
Mahogany, Cherry, Teak, Rosewood. Tops — Wood,
Glass, Carrara Glass, Colored Lacquer, Mosaic
Designer: Vladimir Kagan
Manufacturer: Kagan-Dreyfuss, Inc.

No. 331   Round Table
Diameter 24″   Height 19″
Material: Oil-finished Walnut Top. Solid
    Walnut Legs. Black Steel Brackets
Designer: Allan Gould
Manufacturer: Allan Gould Designs, Inc.

No. 49T   Card Table
Length 35½″   Depth 35½″   Height 29″
Material: Walnut Construction. Tops — Wood,
    Formica, or Marble in Six Variations
Designer: Robert Balonick
Manufacturer: Marden Mfg., Inc.

No. 942 "Fossil-Stone" Table
Material: "Fossil-Stone" Top. Brass Base
Designer: Harvey Probber
Manufacturer: Harvey Probber, Inc.

No. 118   Occasional Table
Diameter 36"   Height 29"
Material: Top — White Carrara
Marble Striated with
Gold-flecked Black.
Wrought Iron Base
Designer and
Manufacturer: Rene Brancusi, Inc.

No. 120   Magazine-Coffee Table
Length 60"   Height 20"
Material: Carrara Marble Top. Walnut Magazine Rack.
Brass Legs
Designer and Manufacturer: Rene Brancusi, Inc.

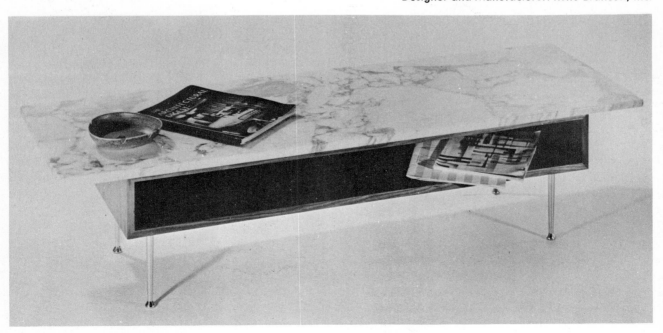

No. 119　Strut Base Occasional Table
Diameter 18"　Height 15"
Material: Carrara Marble Top. Brass Base
Designer: Martin Perfit
For Rene Brancusi, Inc.

No. 213　Cafe Table
Diameter 29"　Height 27½"
Material: Plastic Top.
　Black Steel Pedestal
Manufacturer: Allan Gould
　Designs, Inc.

No. 8131　Cigarette Table
Diameter 17"　Height 21"
Material: Top — Glass, Marble or
　Wood. Maple Base
Designer: Leonard Simmen
Manufacturer: Erwin-Lambeth, Inc.

No. 5313　Table
Length 25½"　Width 25"　Height 22"
Material: Mahogany Base. Sap Walnut Top
Designer: Edward J Wormley
Manufacturer: Dunbar Furniture
　Corporation of Indiana

No. 2132   Table
Length 28″   Width 22″   Height 24″
Material: Walnut or Walnut Veneer.
Top — Plastic,
in White or Walnut
Designer: Bertha Schaefer
Manufacturer: M. Singer & Sons

No. T-3   Table
Diameter 22″   Height 21″
Material: Glass or White Carrara Top.
Brass Base
Designer: Ernest Lowy
Manufacturer: Koch & Lowy Mfg. Co.

No. 313   Stem Table
Length 15″   Width 15″
Height 22½″
Material: Solid Walnut or White
Plastic Top.
Black Steel Pedestal
Designer: Allan Gould
Manufacturer: Allan Gould
Designs, Inc.

No. 3161   Magazine Table
Material: Rock Maple
Designer: Milo Baughman
Manufacturer: Murray Furniture
Manufacturing Company

No. 500   Breakfront-Divider
Length 60"   Depth 20"   Height 84"
Material: Walnut with White Micarta Top
Designer: Paul Colby
Manufacturer: Colby Associates

No. 9705   Irwin Room Divider
Length 60″   Depth 13″   Height 60″

No. 9305   Low Server
Length 60″   Depth 19″   Height 16″

Material: Brass Framing with Mahogany. Finishes —
   Sandrift, Walnut, Teak and Saffron
Designer: Paul McCobb Design Associates
Manufacturer: Calvin Furniture Co.

No. 65018   Door Height Divider
Height 80"
Material: Walnut. "Marba-Rok" Lower Shelf
Designers: Stewart MacDougall, Kipp Stewart
Manufacturer: Glenn of California

No. 962   Gate-Leg Room Divider
Length (shelves) 72"   Depth 12"   Height 72"
Materials: Nova-Ply Shelves. Metal Frame
Designers: Hendrik Van Keppel and Taylor Green
Manufacturer: Van Keppel-Green

No. 5650　China Top
Length (top) 50⅜"　Length (base) 47¾"
Depth 13"　Height 31¼"
Material: Mahogany. Glass Doors

No. 5642　Buffet
Length 50"　Depth 19"　Height 30⅞"
Material: Mahogany. Brass Ferrules and Trim Strips

Designer: J. Gordon Perlmutter
Manufacturer: The Brandt Cabinet Works Inc.

No. 3341   Wall Cabinet
Base Unit: Length 68″   Depth 16¼″   Height 32″
Deck Unit: Length 64¾″   Depth 15¼″   Height 36″
Material: Walnut. Finishes — Sorrel, Sienna, Sherry, Saffron,
   Cordovan
Designer: T. H. Robsjohn-Gibbings
Manufacturer: The Widdicomb Furniture Company

Irwin Breakfront

No. 8006   Breakfront Top
Length 72"   Depth 14"   Height 50"

No. 8506   Cabinet Base
Length 72"   Depth 19"   Height 34"

Material: Brass and Mahogany. Finishes — Sandrift,
Walnut, Teak and Saffron
Designer: Paul McCobb Design Associates
Manufacturer: Calvin Furniture Co.

R6 Cabinet
Length 36″ Depth 14″ Height 24″
Material: Birch or Walnut. Glass Doors

R12 Case
Length 54″ Depth 21″ Height 24″
Material: Birch or Walnut. Plastic Strip Tambour
Doors. Brass Legs

Designer: Jens Risom
Manuacturer: Jens Risom Design, Inc.

No. 5578   Sideboard
Length 61"   Depth (top) 8¼"   (serving top) 17½"
(bottom) 19"   Height (over-all) 75½"
Material: Mahogany with Heavy-textured Rabannas Doors
Designer: Edward J Wormley
Manufacturer: Dunbar Furniture Corporation of Indiana

No. 5630   Room Divider or Hutch
Length (top) 52½"   (base) 49⅝"   Depth 17"   Height 34"

No. 5640   Buffet
Length 56"   Depth 19"   Height 30¼"

Material: Figured Mahogany Veneer. Solid Mahogany
Base and Spindles. Brass Ferrules and Trim
Designer: J. Gordon Perlmutter
Manufacturer: The Brandt Cabinet Works, Inc.

No. 7020   Secretary Unit
Length 37"   Depth (lower cabinet) 18"
(upper part) 12"   Height (over-all) 76"
Material: Mahogany. Finishes — Sandrift, Walnut,
Teak, Saffron. Brass Stretcher. Cane Doors
Designer: Paul McCobb Design Associates
Manufacturer: H. Sacks and Sons

No. 3331   China Deck
Length 54″   Depth 13½″   Height 31½″

No. 5330   Buffet
Length 65″   Depth 20″   Height 30″

Material: Oak with Cane Doors
Designer: Herbert Ten Have
Manufacturer: Sligh Furniture

No. Ry-20   Sideboard
Length 71"   Depth (top) 14½"   (base) 14½"
Height (over-all) 71"   (base) 29"
Material: Oak with Woven Cane Doors or Teak
with Teak Doors
Designer: Hans J. Wegner
For George Tanier, Inc.

No. 147 Commode
Length 66″   Depth 17″   Height 31½″
Material: White Lacquered. Brass Hardware.
Dark Mahogany Base
Designer: Tommi Parzinger
For Parzinger Originals, Inc.

No. 9315   Server
Length 60"   Depth 19"   Height 29"
Material: Brass Base. Roman Travertine Marble Top.
 Mahogany Shelves and Drawers. Finishes —
 Sandrift, Teak, Walnut and Saffron
Designer: Paul McCobb Design Associates
Manufacturer: Calvin Furniture Company

No. 7902/5   High Base with Drawer Unit
Length 65"   Depth 18"   Height 29¾"
Material: Mahogany with Cane Shelf

No. 7906   Cabinet
Length 36"   Depth 18"   Height 26"
Material: Mahogany

Designer: Greta Grossman
Manufacturer: Glenn of California

No. 5632　Chest
Length 32″　Depth 18″
Height (with legs) 29″　(without legs) 22″
Material: Figured Mahogany Veneer

No. 5629　Cocktail Table
Length 50″　Depth 21″　Height 14¾″
Material: Figured Cherry Veneered Top Banded
in Mahogany. Mahogany Rim and Legs

Designer: J. Gordon Perlmutter
Manufacturer: The Brandt
Cabinet Works, Inc.

No. 8632TB　Buffet on Base (or on legs)
Length 65″　Height 37″
Material: Mahogany (or with travertine top)
Wood or Fabric Covered Door Panels
Designers: Kipp Stewart and Stewart MacDougall
Manufacturer: Glenn of California

No. 7026   Cabinet
Length 24"   Depth 18"   Height 34"

No. 7023   Cabinet
Length 36"   Depth 18"   Height 34"

No. 7025   Cabinet
Length 24"   Depth 18"   Height 34"

Material: Mahogany. Finishes — Sandrift, Walnut, Teak,
and Saffron. Brass Legs
No. 7023   Cabinet is Bar Unit Lined with White Formica
Designer: Paul McCobb Design Associates
Manufacturer: H. Sacks & Sons

No. 5520 Buffet
Length 80" Depth 18¼" Height 26"
Material: Rosewood with Cast Aluminum Legs
Designer: George Nelson
Manufacturer: Herman Miller Furniture Company

No. 7707   Cane Door Chest
Length 72"   Depth 19"   Height 34"
Material: Mahogany. Finishes — Sandrift, Walnut, Teak,
    Saffron. Wood Top or Leather Top with Brass Edges
Designer: Paul McCobb Design Associates
Manufacturer: Calvin Furniture Co.

No. 5641   China Top
Length 53"   Depth 13"   Height 40"
Material: Figured Mahogany Veneer

No. 5640   Buffet
Length 56"   Depth 19"   Height 30¼"
Material: Figured Mahogany Veneer with Solid
Mahogany Tambour Front. Solid Mahogany
Base with Brass Ferrules and Trim

Designer: J. Gordon Perlmutter
Manuacturer: The Brandt Cabinet Works Inc.

No. 40-1   Sideboard
Length 78"   Depth 18"   Height 30"
Material: Teak with Cane Doors
Designer: Finn Juhl
Manufacturer: Baker Furniture, Inc.

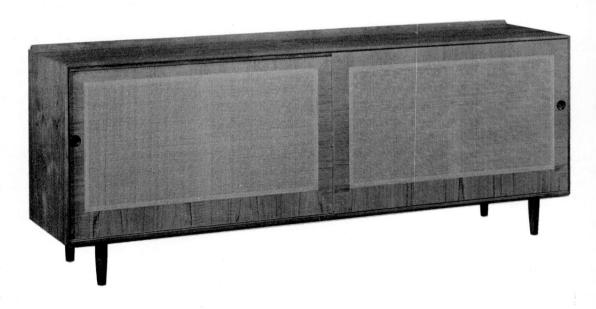

M1147   M1156   M1144   Cabinets
Length 64″   Depth 18″   Height 64″
Material: Quartered Teak Veneer. Cane Doors.
Brass Legs 6″ or 9″
Designer: Harold M. Schwartz
Manufacturer: Romweber

No. 5463   Sideboard
Length 52"   Depth 23¼"   Height 40"
Material: Tawi Fronts. Mahogany Case. Marble Top.
    Brass Base
Designer: Edward J Wormley
Manufacturer: Dunbar Furniture Corporation of Indiana

No. 4029   Sideboard
Length 56″   Depth 21″   Height 33″

No. 4039   Silver Cabinet
Length 52″   Depth 16″   Height 6¼″

Material: Grained Cherry
Designer: William L. Beard
Manufacturer: Statton Furniture Manufacturing Company

No. 5518   Television and Hi-Fi Unit
Length 80″   Depth 23″   Height 28″
Material: Rosewood
Designer: George Nelson
Manufacturer: Herman Miller Furniture Company

No. 3359   Wall Cabinet
Length 69"   Depth 17"   Height 67"
Material: Walnut. Finishes — Sorrel, Sherry, Sienna
Designer: T. H. Robsjohn-Gibbings
Manufacturer: The Widdicomb Furniture Company

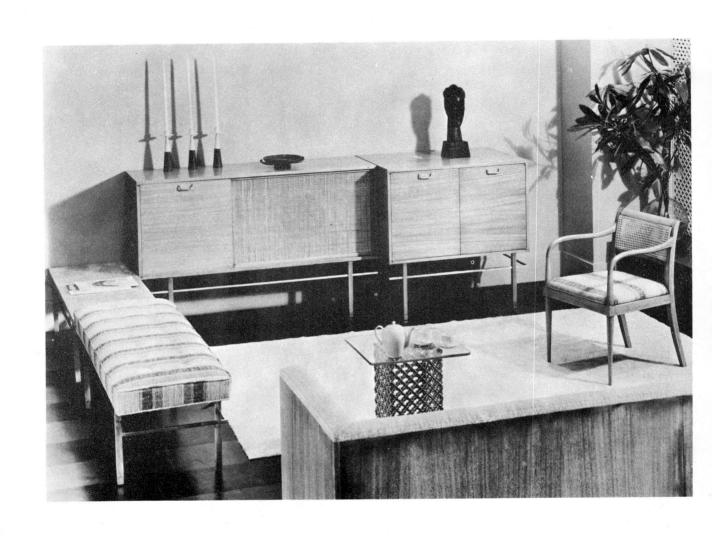

No. 738, No. 798   Hi-Fi Television Combination
Material: Pierced Mahogany, Natural Cane and Brass
Designer: Harvey Probber
Manufacturer: Harvey Probber, Inc.

No. SD36   Cabinet
Length 36″   Depth 18″   Height 34″
Material: Maple, Walnut. Walnut Oil Finish
Designer: Allan Gould
Manufacturer: Allan Gould Designs, Inc.

No. 30 WCM   Cabinet
Length 30″   Depth 18″   Height (without legs) 24″
Material: Solid Birch. Miramica Top.
   Wood Doors. Metal Legs
Designer: Marc Berge
Manufacturer: Berge-Norman Associates, Inc.

No. 3020　Storage Unit
Length 65"　Height 15"
Material: Walnut. Three Pandanus-covered Doors

No. 3021　Platform
Length 65"　Height 15"
Material: Black or Red Frame

Designer: Milo Baughman
Manufacturer: Glenn of California

No. 7706　Leather Door Chest
Length 72"　Depth 19"　Height 34"
Material: Mahogany. Finishes — Sandrift, Teak, Walnut,
　Saffron. Top — Wood, Marble, or Leather with Brass
　Edging. Brass Base
Designer: Paul McCobb Design Associates
Manufacturer: Calvin Furniture Co.

No. 470   Cabinet
Length 96"   Depth 18"   Height 30"
Material: Teak. Natural Oil Finish
Designer: Darrell Landrum
For Avard

No. B-60-6-M   Chest
Length 60″   Depth 18″   Height 24″ (without legs)
Material: Solid Birch. Miramica Top. Metal Legs
Designer: Marc Berge
Manufacturer: Berge-Norman Associates, Inc.

No. 4034   Steel Frame Case
Length 34″   Depth 17″   Height 29½″
Material: Lacquered Steel. Plastic Shelves
Designer: George Nelson
Manufacturer: Herman Miller Furniture Company

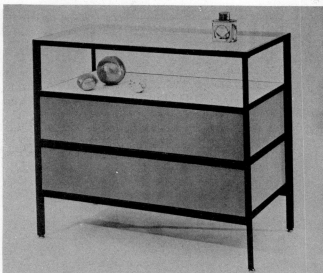

No. 4021   Steel Frame Case
Length 34″   Depth 17″   Height 29½″
Material: Lacquered Steel. Glass Top.
    Plastic Shelves
Designer: George Nelson
Manufacturer: Herman Miller Furniture Company

No. 226-2   Chest
Length 37″   Depth 19½″   Height 29-5/16″
Material: Teak Top. White Lacquer Front.
    White Plastic Ends and Back
Designer: Knoll Planning Unit
Manufacturer: Knoll Associates, Inc.

No. 5531   Chest
Length 64"   Depth 18"   Height 34"
Material: Figured White Cherry. Brass and
    White Cherry Pedestals
Designer: Edward J Wormley
Manufacturer: Dunbar Furniture Corporation of Indiana

No. 401 Cabinet
Length 54"   Depth 14"   Height 30"
Material: Hardwood Lacquer Finish.
   Brushed Chrome Legs
Designer: Darrell Landrum
For Avard

No. 4728 Cabinet
Length 50"   Depth 16"   Height 20"
Material: Mahogany. White Lacquer Door
Designer: Lorin Jackson
Manufacturer: Imperial Furniture Company

No. 5016   Drawer Unit
Length 69½"   Depth 21¼"   Height 32¼"
Material: Walnut. Finishes — Sorrel, Sienna, Sherry,
   Saffron, Cordovan
Designer: T. H. Robsjohn-Gibbings
Manufacturer: The Widdicomb Furniture Company

No. 556   Chest
Length 56"   Depth 20"   Height 32"
Material: Walnut or Birch. Madagascar Wood
or Cane Panel
Designer: Paul Colby
Manufacturer: Colby Associates

No. L10   Cabinet
Length 33"   Depth 18"   Height 29"
Material: Walnut with White Plastic Top
Designer: Allan Gould
Manufacturer: Allan Gould Designs, Inc.

No. 3000 FH   Cabinet
Length 72"   Depth 18"   Height 30"
Material: Walnut or Birch. Formica Top
Designer and Manufacturer: Smilow-Thielle

186

No. 226-1   Chest
Length 37"   Depth 19½"   Height 29-5/16"
Material: Teak Front and Ends. White Plastic
    Laminated Top and Back
Designer: Knoll Planning Unit
Manufacturer: Knoll Associates, Inc.

No. 912   Double Dresser
Material: Mahogany. Smoke Finish.
Brass Stretcher Base
Designer: Harvey Probber
Manufacturer: Harvey Probber, Inc.

No. 5522   Wall Hi-Fi Unit
Length 62"   Depth 16½"   Height 16⅝"
Material: Rosewood Face. Walnut Backing
Designer: George Nelson
Manufacturer: Herman Miller Furniture Company

No. 226-1 Chests
Length (over-all) 102"   Depth 19½"   Height 29-5/16"
Material: White Plastic Tops and Backs. Teak Fronts and Ends

No. 229-1   Suspended Vanity
Length 28"   Depth 19½"
Material: Teak Front. White Plastic Laminated Top

Designer: Knoll Planning Unit
Manufacturer: Knoll Associates, Inc.

No. 5325   Wardrobe
Length 44"   Depth 20"   Height 48"
Material: Oak. Finishes — Acorn, Charcoal, Platinum, or
   Weathered.
Designer: Herbert Ten Have
Manufacturer: Sligh Furniture

No. 7704   Men's High Chest
Length 48"   Depth 19"   Height 48"
Material: Mahogany. Finishes — Sandrift, Walnut,
Teak, Saffron. Brass Trim
Designer: Paul McCobb Design Associates
Manufacturer: Calvin Furniture Co.

No. OS 26   Man's Chest
Length 36"   Depth 19½"   Height 19¼"
Material: Teak. Oak Base
Designer: Arne Vodder
For George Tanier, Inc.

No. R. 12   with Bar Shelf
Length 54"   Depth 21"   Height 24"
Material: Birch or Walnut. Micarta Shelf
Designer: Jens Risom
Manufacturer: Jens Risom Design, Inc.

No. 5640-A   High Cabinet
Length 51″   Depth 14″   Height 76″
Material: Sap Green Walnut Doors. Natural
Green Walnut Case. White Lacquer Interior.
Back Attached to Wall
Designer: Edward J Wormley
Manufacturer: Dunbar Furniture Corp. of Indiana

No. 5469   High Cabinet
Length 40″   Depth 20″   Height 67″
Material: Tawi Fronts. Mahogany Case. Brass
Base. Plastic Laminated Panels in Doors. Marble Top
Designer: Edward J Wormley
Manufacturer: Dunbar Furniture Corporation of Indiana

No. 4049   Bar Server
Length 30″   Depth 19″   Height 35″
Material: Cherry. Brown Finish
Designer: William L. Beard
Manufacturer: Statton Furniture Mfg. Company

No. 7023   Bar Unit
Length 36"   Depth 18"   Height 34"
Material: Mahogany. Finishes — Walnut,
    Teak, Sandrift
Designer: Paul McCobb
Manufacturer: H. Sacks & Sons

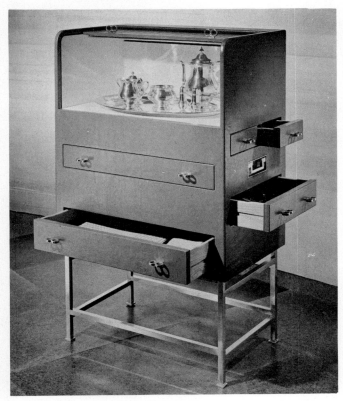

No. 5434   Silver Chest
Custom Built
Length 28"   Depth 18"   Height 48"
Material: Leather Covered. Brass Base.
    Tambour Top. Polished Brass
Designer: Edward J Wormley
Manufacturer: Dunbar Furniture Corp. of Indiana

No. 600   Hi-Fi Cabinet
Length 70"   Depth 20"   Height 30"
Material: Walnut. Separate Speaker
with Madagascar Front
Designer: Paul Colby
Manufacturer: Colby Associates

No. 5518 Hi-Fi Cabinet
Material: Rosewood

No. 5519 Hi-Fi Cabinet
Material: Walnut

Length 80″ Depth 23″ Height 35″
Designer: George Nelson
Manufacturer: Herman Miller Furniture Company

No. S.624   T.V.-Radio-Phonograph Cabinet
Length 52"   Depth 23"   Height 48"
Material: Birch or Walnut. Plastic Panel.
   Pandanus Cloth on Speaker
Designer: Jens Risom
Manufacturer: Jens Risom Design, Inc.

No. HF-1   Hi-Fidelity Cabinet
Length 48"   Depth 12"   Height 32"
Material: Walnut or Birch. Threaded
Wrought Iron Supports
Designer and Manufacturer: Smilow-Thielle

No. 836   Phono Unit (Hi-Fidelity)
Length 36"   Depth 18"   Height 34"
Material: Wood Door in Front of Preamplifier.
Finishes — Sandrift, Walnut, Teak, Mahogany
and Blond. Speaker Material: Natural Cane.
Control Panel Background: Black Leather,
Aluminum or Base Plate
Designer: Paul McCobb Design Associates
Manufacturer: Bell and Howell

No. 872   Radio-Phono-Tape Recorder
   Hi-Fidelity Unit
Length 72"   Depth 19"   Height 34"
Material: Accordian Fold Doors.
   Finishes — Sandrift, Walnut, Teak, Mahogany
and Blond. Speaker Material: Natural Caning.
   Control Panel Background: Black Leather
with Brass or Aluminum
Designer: Paul McCobb Design Associates
Manufacturer: Bell and Howell

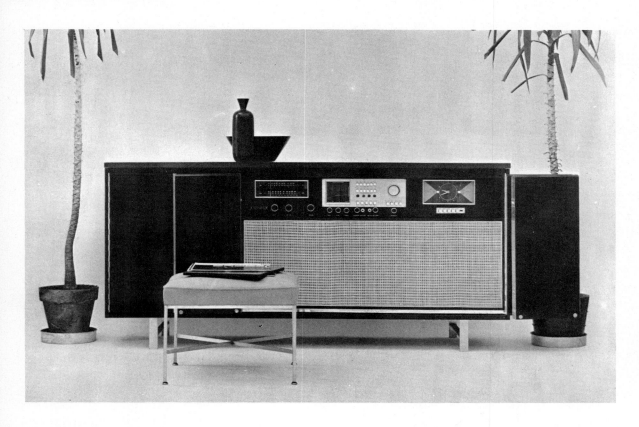

SOFASANDBEDSSOFASANDBEDSSOFASANDBEDSSOFASANDBEDSSOFASANDBEDSSOFASANDE

No. 57   Modular Sofa
Length 81″   Depth 30″   Height 27″
Material: Foam Rubber Seat Cushions.
  Aluminum or Brass Finish Legs
Designer: Paul McCobb Design Associates
Manufacturer: Custom Craft, Inc.

No. 5316   Sofa
Length 90″   Depth 30½″   Height 28½″
Material: Mahogany Frame
Designer: Edward J Wormley
Manufacturer: Dunbar Furniture Corporation of Indiana

No. 676   Sofa
Length 79½"   Depth 30"   Height 29½"
Material: Natural Walnut or Maple Base. Webbing
    Strips on Back Seat and Back Beam Framework.
    Contrasting Wood. Foam Rubber
Designer: Lewis Butler
Manufacturer: Knoll Associates, Inc.

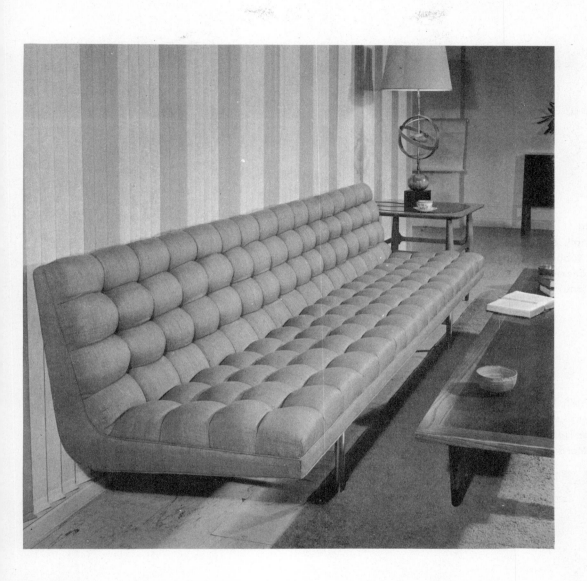

Tufted Sofa
Available in Foot-lengths up to 9'
Material: Spun Brass Legs
Designer: Harold M. Schwartz
Manufacturer: Romweber

No. 7/FC   Sofa
Length 96"   Depth 27½"   Height 27½"
Material: Foam Rubber. Chrome Plated Steel Legs.
   Black Baked Enamel Frame
Designer and Manufacturer: Laverne Originals

No. 359   Sofa
Length 84"   Depth 31½"   Height 31½"
Material: Rubber Cushion and Pillows. Walnut Legs
Designer: Homer Tremulis
Manufacturer: Marden Mfg., Inc.

No. 4906-A   Sofa
Length (over-all) 97"   Depth (over-all) 42"   Height 28½"
Material: Mahogany Legs
Designer: Edward J Wormley
Manufacturer: Dunbar Furniture Corporation of Indiana

No. RAS-444   Sleepsofa
Length 85"   Depth 31"   Height 28"
Material: Floating Steel Platform in Walnut
or Birch Frame. Foam Rubber
Designer and Manufacturer: Smilow-Thielle

No. 5485 Sofa
Length 56" Depth 33" Height 31"
Material: Wood Frame. Cast Aluminum Legs
Designer: George Nelson
Manufacturer: Herman Miller Furniture Company

No. 47   Sofa
Length 85"   Depth 32½"   Height 32"
Material: Foam Rubber Cushions and Pillows
Designer: Paul McCobb Design Associates
Manufacturer: Custom Craft, Inc.

No. 53T   Sofa
Length 84"   Depth 31"   Height 30"
Material: Solid Teak with Foam Rubber
Designer: Florence Knoll
Manufacturer: Knoll Associates, Inc.

No. 407   Sectional Unit
Depth 30"   Height (over-all) 30"   (arm) 22½"
Material: Tight Foam Rubber Seat and Back
Designer: Robert Balonick
Manufacturer: Marden Mfg., Inc.

No. 400   Corner Sofa Unit
Length 72″   Width (unit) 72″   Depth 30″   Height 30″
Material: Loose Foam Rubber Cushion and Rubber Back.
Brass Legs
Designer: Robert Balonick
Manufacturer: Marden Mfg., Inc.

No. 176SC   Floating Seat Sofa
Length 7' to 12'   Depth 32"   Height 28"
Material: Wood Frame. Finishes — Walnut, Cherry, Korina,
    Mahogany, Teak, Rosewood
Designer: Vladimir Kagan
Manufacturer: Kagan-Dreyfuss, Inc.

Multi-Unit Sofa
No. 8051/8057/8053/8060
Material: Maple Legs. Nutmeg Finish
Designer: Barney Flagg
Manufacturer: Edwin-Lambeth, Inc.

No. 613   Settee
Length 60"   Depth 26"
    Height 28"
Material: Solid Wood Frame.
    Foam Rubber Back and Sea[t]
Designer: Allan Gould
Manufacturer: Allan Gould
    Designs, Inc.

No. U.151   Sofa
Length 54"   Depth 31"
    Height 32½"
Material: Birch or Walnut Fra[me]
Designer: Jens Risom
Manufacture: Jens Risom
    Design, Inc.

No. 52   Settee
Length 56"   Depth 31"
Height 30"
Material: Brushed Chrome
Finish Base or
Solid Teak Base.
Foam Rubber Cushions
Designer: Florence Knoll
Manufacturer: Knoll
Associates, Inc.

No. MS-603   Sofa
Length 72"   Depth 30"
Height 32½"
Material: Foam Rubber
Designer: William Armbruster
Manufacturer: Edgewood
Furniture Company, Inc.

No. 358   Sofa
Length 84"   Depth 31"   Height 33"
Material: Wood Legs. Rubber Cushion
Designer: Homer Tremulis
Manufacturer: Marden Mfg., Inc.

No. 164   Sofa
Length 84"   Depth 31"   Height 31½"
Material: Walnut Legs
Designer: Bertha Schaefer
Manufacturer: M. Singer & Sons

No. 682-1AZ   683-1AZ   Sofas
Length (each) 52″   Depth 31½″   Height 30½″
Material: Show-wood Base. Walnut Finish Legs.
Brass Collar and Tip
Designer: Norman Fox MacGregor
Manufacturer: Valley Upholstery Corporation

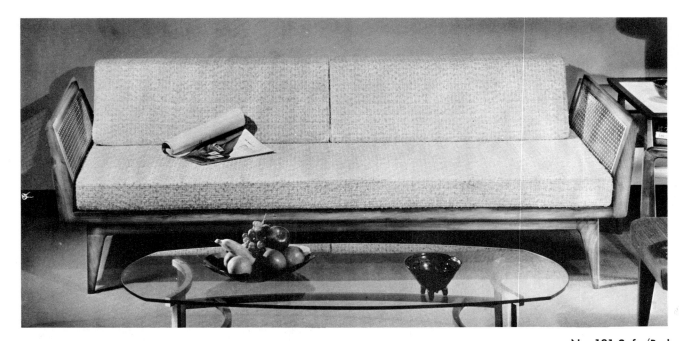

No. 181 Sofa/Bed
Length 82″   Depth 32½″   Height 27½″
Material: Walnut
Designer: Bertha Schaefer
Manufacturer: M. Singer & Sons

No. 2012   Sofa
Length (over-all) 92″   Depth 34″   Height 31″
Material: Walnut Frame
Designer: T. H. Robsjohn-Gibbings
Manufacturer: The Widdicomb Furniture Company

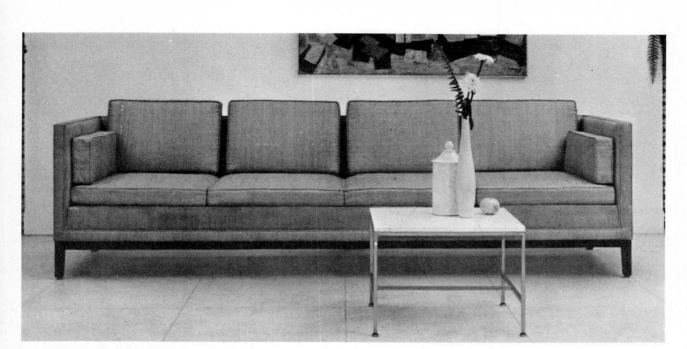

No. 1327   Sofa
Length 96″   Depth 33″   Height 29″
Material: Wood Base. Foam Rubber
Designer: Paul McCobb Design Associates
Manufacturer: Custom Craft, Inc.

No. 160   Sofa
Length 92″   Depth 30″   Height 30″
Material: Brass Legs
Designer: Carlo De Carli
Manufacturer: M. Singer & Sons

No. 5523   Flip-Flop Sofabed
Open as Bed

No. 5523   Flip-Flop Sofabed
Length 84"   Depth 35"   Height 29"
Material: Mahogany Base. Foam Rubber
Designer: Edward J Wormley
Manufacturer: Dunbar Furniture Corporation of Indiana

Sofa Compact
Material: Chrome Plated Steel Base Supports.
Back Can Be Folded to Lie Flat on Seat
Designer: Charles Eames
Manufacturer: Herman Miller Furniture Company

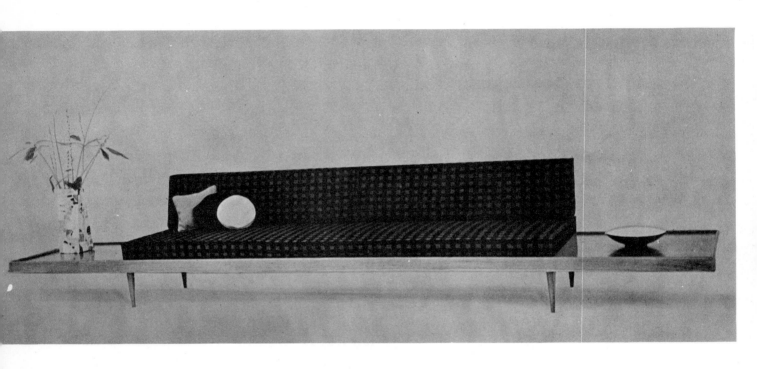

No. 212   Couch
Length (over-all) 11' 4"   Depth 31½"   Height 28"
Material: End Tables and Frame — Walnut, Korina or
    Ebony. Foam Rubber Seating Area Measuring 30" x 75".
    Bolsters—Foam Rubber over Rubberized Hair
Designer: Paul Colby
Manufacturer: Colby Associates

No. 168   Daybed
Length 90"   Depth 27"   Height (over-all) 29"
Material: Birch or Mahogany. End Slab — Birch,
Mahogany or Plastic
Designers: D. R. Bates and Jackson Gregory, Jr.
Manufacturer: Vista Furniture Company

No. 6G Settee
Length (base) 6'
Material: Folding Birch Frame. Micarta Table Top
Designer: George Nelson
Manufacturer: Herman Miller Furniture Company

Caned-end Daybed
Material: Wooden Base. Finishes — Walnut, Cherry,
   Mahogany, Korina, Teak or Rosewood
Designer: Vladimir Kagan
Manufacturer: Kagan-Dreyfuss, Inc.

No. 5415½   Cane Headboard
Height 34"
Material: Cane and Oak in Four Colors —
   Acorn, Weathered, Platinum or Charcoal
Designer: Herbert Ten Have
Manufacturer: Sligh Furniture

No. 802 A   Desk
Material: Mahogany in Eight Finishes
Designer: Harvey Probber
Manufacturer: Harvey Probber, Inc.

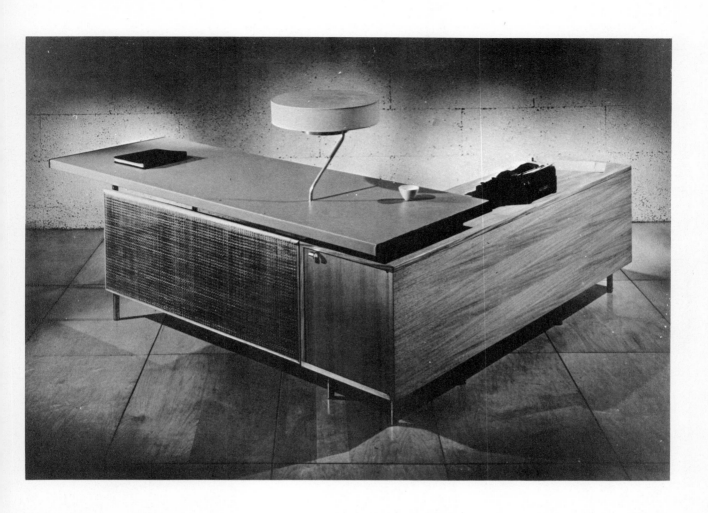

No. 7230 R   Desk with Built-in Lamp
Width 72"   Depth 30"   Height 29½"
Material: Walnut with Woven Cane Front
Designer: George Nelson
Manufacturer: Herman Miller Furniture Company

Secretarial Desk
Top: Width 78"   Depth 30"
Right Pedestal: Width 17"   Depth 27½"   Height 19⅝"
Drawer Unit: Width 17"
Cabinet Unit: Width 88⅝"   Depth 19"   Height 25½"
Material: Walnut. Metal Framing in Brass or Aluminum
Designer: Paul McCobb Design Associates
Manufacturer: H. Sacks & Sons

No. 5500   Desk, Right or Left Hand
Width 60"   Depth 27"   Height 29"
Material: Walnut Top. Mahogany Base

No. 5503   Stationary Pedestal
Width 14½"   Depth 26"   Height 17"
Material: Cane with Mahogany Frame

Designer: Edward J Wormley
Manufacturer: Dunbar Furniture Corporation of Indiana

No. L27   Desk
Width 54"   Depth 48"   Height 29"
Material: Walnut with Plastic Top and Steel Legs
Designer: Allan Gould
Manufacturer: Allan Gould Designs, Inc.

View of Rear

No. 00 500   Fallstaff Desk
Width 47"   Depth 26"   Height 29"
   Drop Leaf 26" x 15½"
Material: Teak Top with Beech Legs or Teak Top with
   Teak-stained or Walnut Legs
Danish Design for George Tanier Inc.

No. 5265 Desk-Table
Closed as Desk

No. 5265   Desk-Table
Length (closed) 60″   (open) 96″   Depth 30″
Height 28″   2 Leaves (each) 18″
Material: Walnut Top. Mahogany Pedestals, Lacquered
    Metal Frame
Designer: Edward J Wormley
Manufacturer: Dunbar Furniture Corporation of Indiana

Open when Used as a Table

No. 3340   Desk
Width 60½"   Depth 23¾"   Height 30½"
Material: Walnut. Finishes — Sienna, Sherry,
   Saffron or Cordovan
Designer: T. H. Robsjohn-Gibbings
Manufacturer: The Widdicomb Furniture Company

Desk For Two People
Width 84"   Depth 29½"   Wall Hung
Material: Walnut. White Formica Top
Finish — Lacquer with Oil Effect
Designer: Rex Goode
Manufacturer: Charles Pechanec, Jr.

No. M-1160   Desk
Width 42"   Depth 24"   Height 29"
Material: Quartered Teak Veneer
Designer: Harold M. Schwartz
Manufacturer: Romweber

No. BO 85   Desk
Width 61"   Depth 21" and 45"
Height 27½"
Material: Teak Top. Beech Legs
Designer: Arne Vodder
For George Tanier, Inc.

No. 510 Modular Group

No. 510-C Cabinet   No. 510-B Bookshelf Unit
No. 510-WL Writing Shelf   No. 510-D Drawer Unit
No. 510-H3 Drawer Unit

Length (over-all) 93"   Depth (cabinet) 16"
Height (over-all) 59"

Material: Walnut or Teak Finish Throughout
(without black frame as pictured)
Designer: Bertil Fridhagen
Manufacturer: Dux AB Sweden
For Dux Incorporated

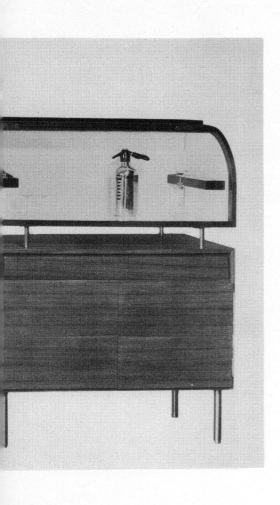

No. M-1141   M-1149   M-1145   M-1143
M-1165   M-1146   Left to Right
Desk and Cabinets
M-1141: Width 24"
M-1149: Width 21"   Depth 36"
M-1145: Width 24"
M-1143: Width 40"
M-1146: Width 40"
M-1165: Width 40"
Material: Quartered Teak Veneer.
Brass Legs and Hardware
Finish: Natural or Dark Wax
Designer: Harold M. Schwartz
Manufacturer: Romweber

No. 4041   Pedestal Desk
Width 44″   Depth 24″   Height 30″
Material: Walnut and Pecan
Finish: Oriental Walnut
Designer and Manufacturer: Sligh Furniture

No. K 71   Lady's Desk
Width 34″   Depth 26½″   Height 34½″
Material: Walnut with White Tambour Door
Finish: Walnut or Charcoal
Designer: John Van Koert
Manufacturer: Drexel Furniture Company

No. DE-10   Extension Desk
Width (closed) 48″   (open) 60″
Depth 24″   Height 29″
Material: Walnut or Birch with Formica Top
Designer and Manufacturer: Smilow-Thielle

No. R 14 and R 94   Case With Desk Insert
Width 54″   Depth 21″   Height 31½″
Material: Walnut or Birch
Designer: Jens Risom
Manufacturer: Jens Risom Design, Inc.

No. 5646   Desk
Width 48"   Depth 24"   Height 29½"
Material: Mahogany Veneer
with Cherry Veneer Top Banded
in Solid Mahogany
Designer: J. Gordon Perlmutter
Manufacturer: The Brandt Cabinet Works Inc.

No. 5636, 5635, 5637, 5638
Desk Combination
Width 64"   Depth (top) 13"
(bottom) 18"   Height 62¾"
Material: Mahogany Veneer with
Solid Mahogany Rim and Legs
Designer: J. Gordon Perlmutter
Manufacturer: The Brandt Cabinet
Works Inc.

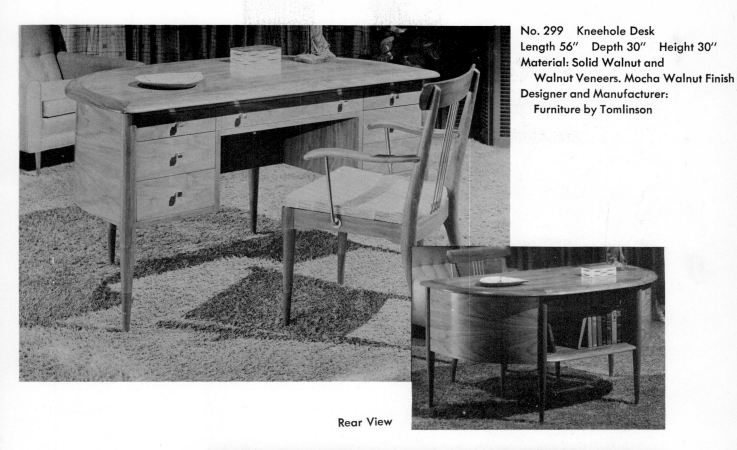

No. 299   Kneehole Desk
Length 56"   Depth 30"   Height 30"
Material: Solid Walnut and
   Walnut Veneers. Mocha Walnut Finish
Designer and Manufacturer:
   Furniture by Tomlinson

Rear View

No. 5123   Desk
Width 60"   Depth 26"   Height 30"
Material: Mahogany with White
   Formica Top
Designer: Lorin Jackson
Manufacturer: Imperial
   Furniture Company

No. 5385   Secretary
Width 30"   Depth 17"   Height 66"
Material: Oak. Finishes — Acorn, Weathered,
Platinum or Charcoal
Designer: Herbert Ten Have
Manufacturer: Sligh Furniture

No. AI-1011   Lady's Desk
Width 35"   Depth 25"   Height 28"
Material: Walnut with Suede Cloth Top
Designer: Ico Parisi
Manufacturer: V. Bega & Figli for Altamira

No. 5472   Writing Table
Width 64"   Depth 30"   Height 29"
Material: Tawi Wood Top. Mahogany Base with
    Brass Shoes and Stretchers
Designers: Edward J Wormley
Manufacturer: Dunbar Furniture Corporation of Indiana

No. 333 Desk
Width 50" Depth 22" Height 28
Material: Plastic Top. Iron Legs
Designer: D. R. Bates and
   Jackson Gregory, Jr.
Manufacturer: Vista Furniture Comp

No. 6200 Desk
Width 48" Depth 24" Height 28½"
Material: Walnut or Walnut
   with Black or White Plastic
Designer: Greta Grossman
Manufacturer: Glenn of California

No. 120 Desk
Width 45″ Depth 18″ Height 29″
Material: Walnut with Plastic Top.
Black Steel Legs
Designer: Allan Gould
Manufacturer: Allan Gould
Designs, Inc.

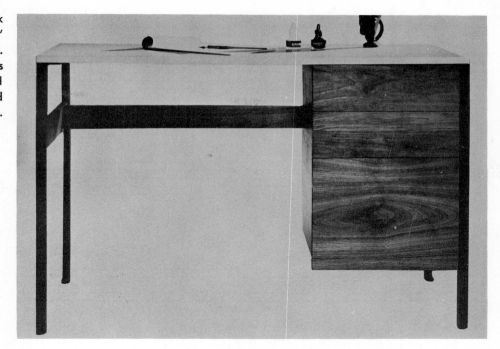

No. 4033 Chest Desk
Width 53⅝″ Depth 18″ Height 30″
Materials: Philippine Mahogany,
Natural or Tawny Birch,
or Plastic. Metal Frame and Legs
Designers: D. R. Bates and Jackson Gregory, Jr.
Manufacturer: Vista Furniture Company

Left
No. 8904   Floor Lamp
Height (adjustable) 45" to 57"   Parabolic Shade 16"
Material: Metal — Ebony Finish and Brass
Designer and Manufacturer: Lightolier, Inc.

Middle
No. 215   Drum Floor Lamp
Height (over-all) 56"   Diameter (shade) 14"
Material: Polished Brass
Designer: T. H. Robsjohn-Gibbings
Manufacturer: The Widdicomb Furniture Company

Right
No. 9729   Floor Lamp
Height (over-all) 57"   (shade) 10"
Material: Walnut Inlaid with Brass
Designer: Gerald Thurston
Manufacturer: Lightolier, Inc.

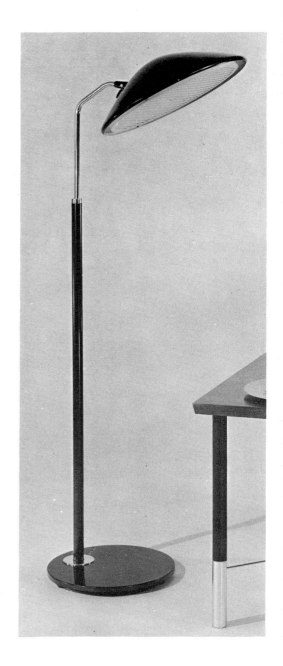

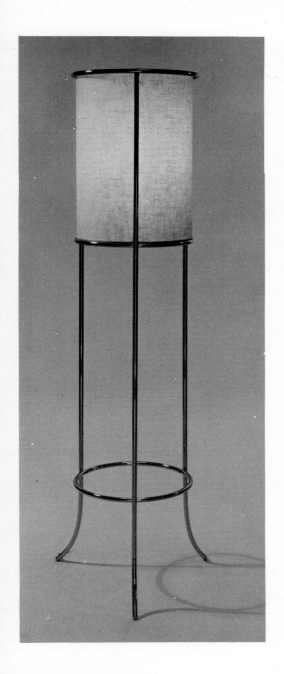

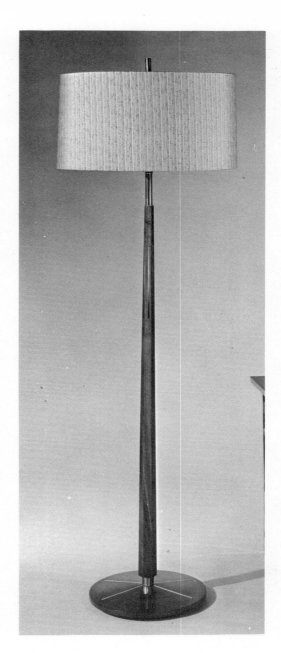

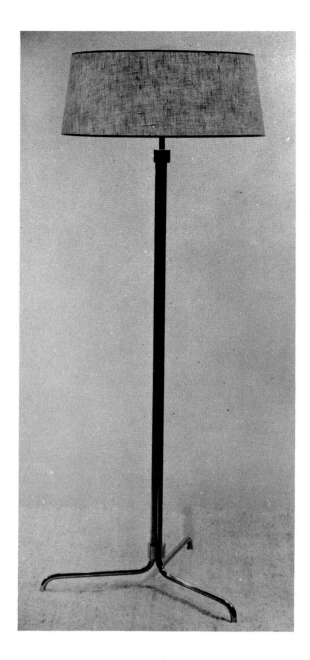

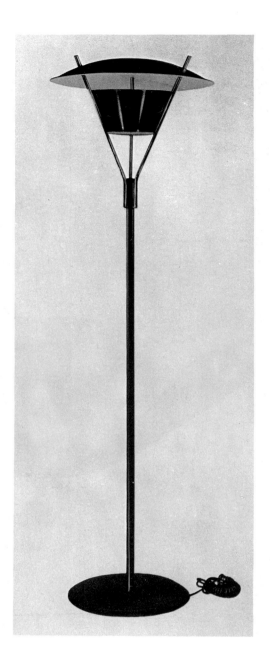

No. 220   Floor Lamp
Height (over-all) 47"   Diameter (shade) 17"
Material: Polished Chrome with Brass Joints
Designer: T. H. Robsjohn-Gibbings
Manufacturer: The Widdicomb Furniture Company

No. 4531   Floor Lamp
Height 66"   Diameter (reflector) 20"
Material: Finished in Black and Brass
Designer: Thomas Moser
Manufacturer: Lightolier, Inc.

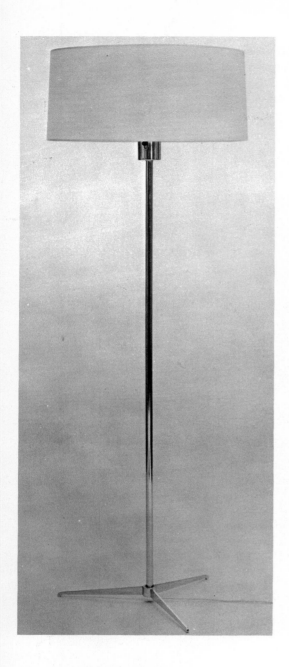

No. 1039   Floor Lamp
Material: Polished Brass
Designer: Ernest Lowy
Manufacturer: Koch & Lowy Mfg. Co.

No. N. S. 924
Height (over-all) 48"   (extended) 67"   (shade) 16"
    Stem Extendable
Material: Satin Chrome and Brushed or Polished Brass
Designer and Manufacturer: Nessen Studio, Inc.

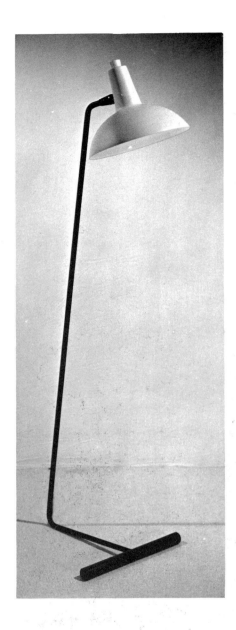

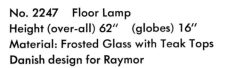

No. 2247   Floor Lamp
Height (over-all) 62"   (globes) 16"
Material: Frosted Glass with Teak Tops
Danish design for Raymor

No. F9   Floor Lamp
Height (over-all) 46"
Material: Spun Aluminum. Black Steel Rod Base
Designer: Harry Gitlin
Manufacturer: Middletown Manufacturing Company

No. 9732   Floor Lamp
Height 66"
Material: Brass. Finishes — Ebony, Walnut and Polished Brass
Designer: Thomas Moser
Manufacturer: Lightolier, Inc.

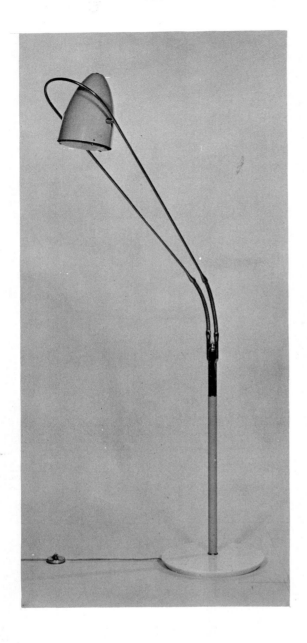

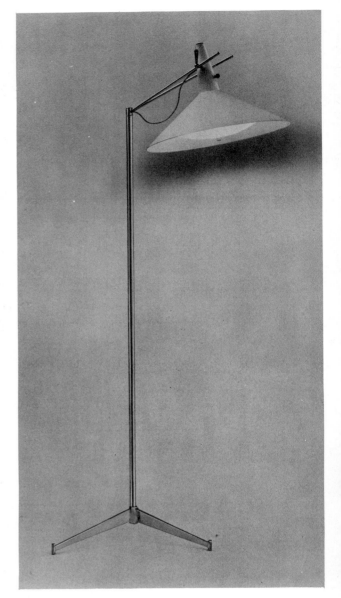

No. AR 12340   Floor Lamp
Height (over-all) 68"
Material: Marble Base. Brass Flexible Stem
Italian design for Altamira

No. E-11   Floor Lamp
Material: Brass Base. White Painted Aluminum Reflector
Designer: Paul McCobb Design Associates
Manufacturer: Excelsior Art Studios

No. 1038   Floor Lamp
Material: Polished Brass Base and Stem
Designer: Ernest Lowy
Manufacturer: Koch & Lowy Mfg. Co.

No. 900-305   Floor Lamp
Height (over-all) 56"   (shade) 12"
Material: Oak Frame with Metal Shade
Designer: Osten Kristiansson
For George Tanier, Inc.

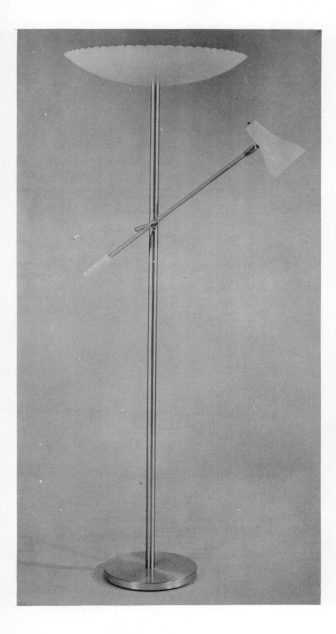

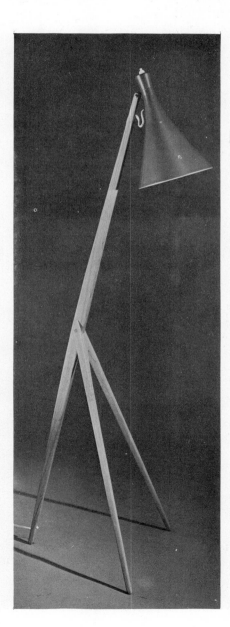

Cylinders
Height 10″ to 24″
    Diameter 4″ to 3″
Designer: Paul Mayen
Manufacturer: Habitat

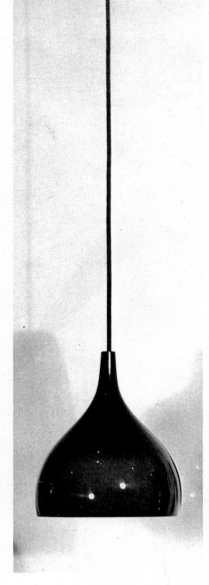

No. AV 4034   Lamp
Height 10½"   Diameter 9½"
Material: Hand Blown Venini Glass
Designer and Manufacturer: Paolo
    Venini
For Altamira

AV 4028   Lamp
Height 11"   Diameter 6"
Material: Hand Blown Venini Glass
Designer and Manufacturer: Paolo Venini
For Altamira

AV 4027
Height 11½"   Diameter 9"
Material: Hand Blown Venini Glass
Designer and Manufacturer: Paolo Venini
For Altamira

No. 10138   Ceiling Fixture
Height (globe) 12"
Material: Opal Globe. Brass Spreader
Designer: Paavo Tynell
For Finland House

No. 40537   "Three in Line" Ceiling Fixture
Material: Brass Yoke. Brass Cylinder on Wire.
Shades of Heavy Textured Cloth
Designer: Gerald Thurston
Manufacturer: Lightolier, Inc.

No. 2213   Ceiling Fixture, Adjustable
Height (over-all globe) 12"
Material: Teak and Frosted Glass
Danish design for Raymor

No. 2088   Ceiling Fixture, Adjustable
Height (over-all globe) 12"
Material: Teak and Frosted White Glass
Danish design for Raymor

No. 2218/5　Ceiling Fixture, Adjustable
Height (over-all globe) 12"
Material: Teak and Frosted Glass
Danish design for Raymor

No. C-19　Ceiling Fixture
Length (stem) 24"
Material: Polished Brass Stem and Rectangular Tubing
Designer: Ernest Lowy
Manufacturer: Koch & Lowy Mfg. Co.

No. 900-525   Ceiling Fixture
Height (globe) 7″   Diameter (over-all) 32″
Material: Oak Crossbar. Opal Glass Globes
Designer: Osten Kristiansson
For Tanier

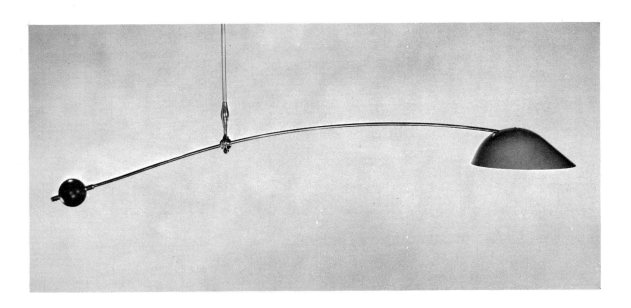

No. AR12432   Hanging Light
Height 52"   Width 66"
Material: Brass Rod and Stem
Manufacturer: Arredoluce
For Altamira

No. 10108   Mobile Ceiling Fixture
Length (body) 40"   Width 30"   Bowl 19"
Material: Solid Brass
Designer: Paavo Tynell
For Finland House

No. 40575   Ceiling Fixture
Width (over-all) 25″   Height (adjustable) 23″ to 56″
Material: Walnut Tripod and Stretcher. Wicker Shades
Designer: Thomas Moser
Manufacturer: Lightolier, Inc.

No. 322   Ceiling Fixture
Height (over-all) 30″
Material: Brushed Aluminum
Designer: Harry Gitlin
Manufacturer: Stamford

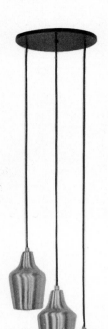

No. 10129/3   Ceiling Fixture
Width (over-all) 41″   Height (shade) 10″
Material: Finishes — Satin Black,
Matt White, Dusk Grey,
Oyster White
Designer: Paavo Tynell
For Finland House

285

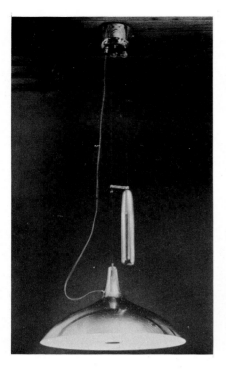

Upper left
No. 10202   Ceiling Fixture
Width 18"   Height (over-all shade) 10"
Material: Solid Brass
Designer: Paavo Tynell
For Finland House

Upper center
No. 40578   Ceiling Fixture
Length (over-all) 55" or 59"
Width 14" or 20"   (globe) 20"
Material: Brass with Wicker Ball
Designer and Manufacturer: Lightolier, Inc.

Upper right
No. 10104   Ceiling Fixture
Width 10"   Height (shade) 10"
Material: Solid Brass
Designer: Paavo Tynell
For Finland House

Lower left
No. 2245   Ceiling Fixture
Width (over-all) 21"   Height (globe) 10¼"
Material: Opal Glass and Polished Brass
Scandinavian design for Raymor

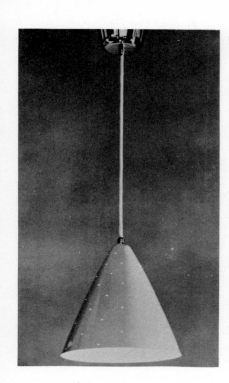

Left
No. 10115   Ceiling Fixture
Height (shade) 10″
Material: Perforated Brass Shade
Designer: Paavo Tynell
For Finland House

Right
Ceiling Fixture
**Material: White Frosted Glass and
   Hand-rubbed Teakwood**
Scandinavian design for Raymor

No. 2219/5   Ceiling Fixture, Adjustable
Length (teak bar) 46″   Height (over-all globe) 16″
Material: Teak and Frosted Glass
Danish design for Raymor

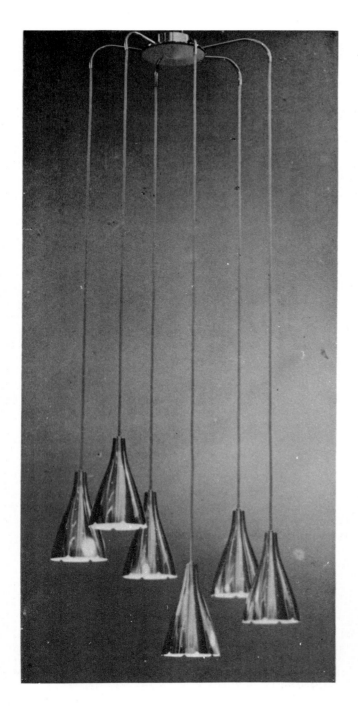

No. 10120   Ceiling Fixture
Width 29½"   Height (shade) 9½"
Material: Finnish Aspenslat Shade. Brass Canopy
Designer: Paavo Tynell
For Finland House

No. 10130/6   Ceiling Fixture
Height (shade) 10"   Width (over-all) 26"
Material: Solid Brass
Designer: Paavo Tynell
For Finland House

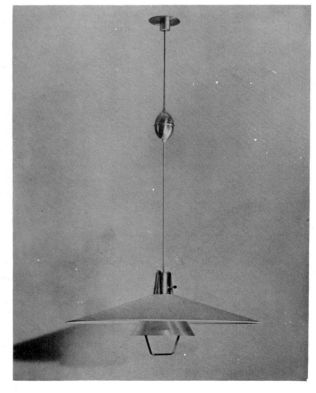

No. 282　Ceiling Fixture
Diameter (shade) 18″
　　(cylinder) 6″
　　Height (over-all) 26″
　　(cylinder) 8″
Material: Opal Glass
　　Cylinder. Frosted
　　Poly-plastic Shade
Designer: Harry Gitlin
Manufacturer: Stamford

No. 40572　Ceiling Fixture
Length (adjustable) 16″ to
　　56″　Width 10″
Material: Wicker. Brass Trimmed
Designer: Thomas Moser
Manufacturer: Lightolier, Inc.

No. 2100　Ceiling Fixture, Adjustable
Height (over-all globe) 12″
Diameter (three-armed teak bar) 12″
　　(each arm 7″ from center)
Material: Teak and Frosted White Glass
　　Danish design for Raymor

Opposite
No. 711　Floating Baffle Lamp
Height (over-all) 14″　Diameter (shade) 30″
Material: Fiberglas Shade. Satin Aluminum Finish
Designer: Richard Kelley
Manufacturer: Middletown Manufacturing Company

289

No. 98-53   Ellipse Chandelier
Height 32″   Diameter 15″
Material: Sections of Crystal with Inside Brass Frame
Designer: Carl Fagerlund
For Hansen

No. AR 12385   Chandelier
Width 21½″   Height 49″
Material: Brass Stem.
White Aluminum Reflector. Black Bullet
Italian design for Altamira

Hanging Lamp
Width 25″   Height 12″
Material: Walnut and Parchment
Designer and Manufacturer: Leslie Larson

No. 3644   Wall Fixture
Material: White Opal Crystal Shades with
Polished Brass Fittings
Danish design for Hansen

No. 9146   Wall Fixture
Length (extension arm) 15″
Material: Baked Enamel or Satin Aluminum Shade
Designer: Kurt Versen
Manufacturer: Kurt Versen Company

No. 4002   Wall Fixture
Diameter (shade) 12″
Material: Brushed Brass, Aluminum or Colored Canopy
   and Stem. Brushed Aluminum or Colored Shade
Designer: Harry Handler
Manufacturer: General Lighting Company

No. 1913
Length 14″ to 31″   Diameter (shade) 12″
Material: Aluminum Canopy and Pantograph. Brushed
   Aluminum or Colored Shade
Designer: Harry Handler
Manufacturer: General Lighting Company

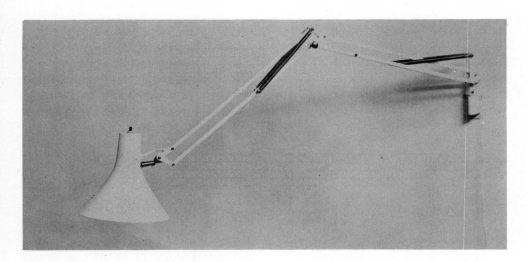

No. NS 965   Wall Fixture
Length (extended) 32″ or 40″
Material: Porcelain Socket in Colors
Designer and Manufacturer: Nessen Studio, Inc.

Wall Lamp
Width 12½″   Height 14″
Material: Mahogany and Parchment
Designer and Manufacturer: Leslie Larson

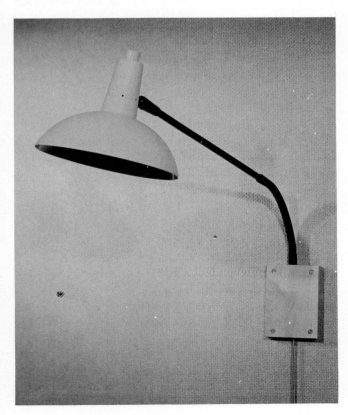

No. W 9   Wall Lamp
Length (over-all extension) 24″
Material: Spun Aluminum Shade. Black Arm.
    Polished Wood Block
Designer: Harry Gitlin
Manufacturer: Middletown Manufacturing Company

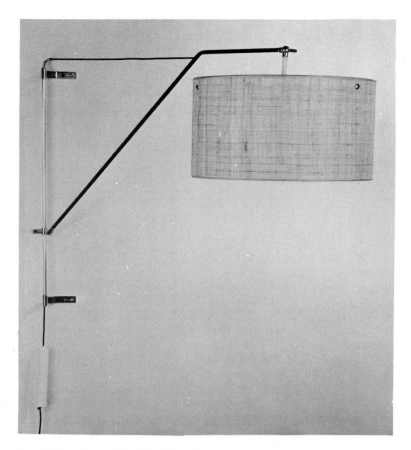

No. 2224   Adjustable Wall Bracket
Length (bracket) 28"   (extended arm) 36"
   Height (shade) 9"
Material: Brass Bracket. Black Arm. White Pulley and Stem.
   Polished Brass Fittings
Italian design for Raymor

No. L&PS 9462   Wall Fixture
Material: Backplate Finished in Sterling Silver Plate
   and Profile. White Fortisan over Fiberglas Shade
Designer: John Van Koert
Manufacturer: Rembrandt Lamp Corp.
   (Colonial-Premier Division)

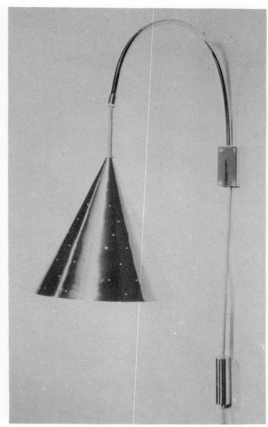

Upper left
No. 900-708   Wall Fixture
Height (shade) 11½"
Material: Metal Shade in Colors. Adjustable Boom of Oak
Designer: Osten Kristiansson
For George Tanier, Inc.

Upper right
No. W-9   Pin-up Lamp, Adjustable
Height (shade) 10"
Material: Polished Brass. Shade in Colors
Designer: Ernest Lowy
Manufacturer: Koch & Lowy Mfg. Co.

Lower right
No. 1950   Wall Fixture
Height (over-all) 14"   Diameter 7"
Material: Glass and Brushed Aluminum
Designer: George Nelson
Manufacturer: General Lighting Company

No. T9   Table Lamp
Height 23"
Material: Spun Aluminum Shade. Steel Base and Stem in
   Flat Black Finish
Designer: Harry Gitlin
Manufacturer: Middletown Manufacturing Company

No. E-7   Desk Lamp
Height (over-all) 23"
Material: Brass Base. White Painted Aluminum Reflector
Designer: Paul McCobb Design Associates
Manufacturer: Excelsior Art Studios

Opposite
No. NS950   Table Lamp
Height (over-all) 18"   Diameter 13"
Material: Polished Brass, Brushed Brass or Satin Chrome
Designer and Manufacturer: Nessen Studio, Inc.

No. 8913   Desk Lamp
Material: Satin-finished Baked Enamel in Colors
Designer and Manufacturer: Litghtolier, Inc.

Table Lamp
Width 16"   Height 12"
Material: Mahogany and Parchment
Designer and Manufacturer: Leslie Larson

Upper right
PYTHAGORAS
Width 52"   Repeat 71"
Material: Hand Print on Linen
Designer: Sven Markelius
Manufacturer: Knoll Textiles, Inc.

Lower left
GEM
Width 53/54"   Repeat 9"
Material: Hand-screen Print on Rayon and Cotton
Designer and Manufacturer: Cohama

Lower right
JAPANESE PAPER
No. 5521
Width 50"   Repeat 33⅜"
Material: Imported Linen
Designer: S. Chermayeff
Manufacturer: L. Anton Maix

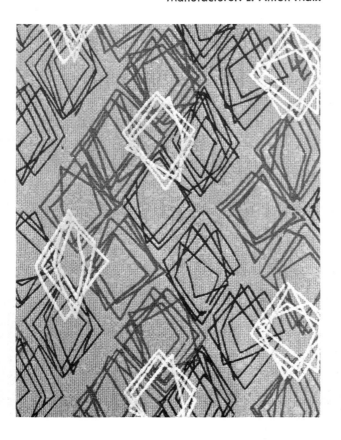

Upper left
TRAPEZE
Width 48"   Repeat 52"
Material: Fiberglas, Batiste and Linen
Designer and Manufacturer: Laverne Originals

Lower left
STRUCTURAL
No. 6270
Width 51"   Repeat 20"
Material: Rayon-backed Linen
Designer: Morris de la Cerda
Manufacturer: Edwin Raphael Company, Inc.

Lower right
SQUARES H. P.
No. 29405
Width 50"
Material: 100% Linen
Designer and Manufacturer: J. H. Thorp & Co., Inc.

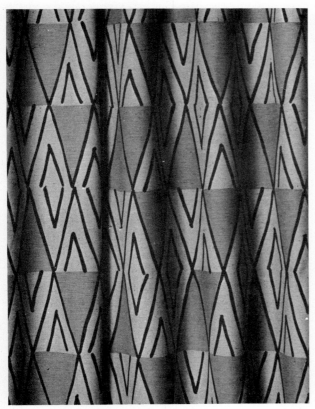

Upper right
RAIN
Nos. 620, 621, 622, 623
Material: Nos. 620, 622 on Linen
Nos. 621, 623 on Silk
Designer: Alexander Girard
Manufacturer: Herman Miller Fabrics

Lower left
DOUBLE TRIANGLES
No. 600
Width 48″
Material: Batiste, Linen and Cotton
Designer: Alexander Girard
Manufacturer: Herman Miller Fabrics

Lower right
RECTANGULAR JAMBOREE
No. 5677
Width 50″
Material: Jacquard Weave
Designer: Adriana Scalamandré
Manufacturer: Scalamandré Silks, Inc.

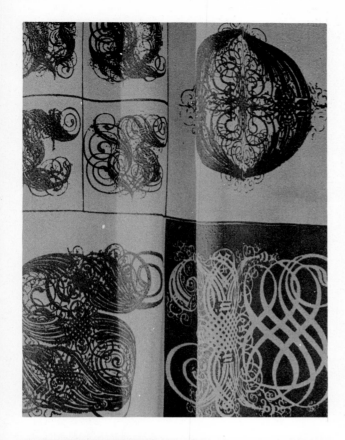

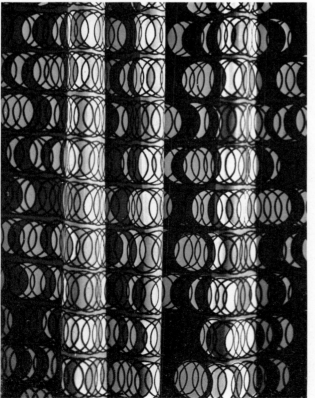

Upper left
ALPHABET
No. 1090
Width 48"   Repeat 36"
Material: Opaque Fiberglas, Boucle Fiberglas,
    Linen Casement or Medium Weight Linen
Designer and Manufacturer: Ben Rose

Upper right
ZEROS
Width 50"   Repeat 6½"
Material: Hand-screened Fabric
Designer: Bernard Rudofsky
Manufacturer: Schiffer Prints Division, Mil-Art Company

Lower left
ECLIPSE
Width 50"   Repeat 27"
Material: Hand-screened Fabric
Designer: Abel Sorensen
Manufacturer: Schiffer Prints Division, Mil-Art Company

Upper right
DIAMONDS
No. 6460
Width 51"   Repeat 19"
Material: Rayon-backed Linen
Designer: Dave Zeese
Manuafcturer: Edwin Raphael Company, Inc.

Lower left
LEXINGTON
Width 50"   Repeat 27"
Material: Hand-screen Fabric
Designer: Freda Diamond
Manufacturer: Schiffer Prints Division, Mil-Art Company

Lower right
FUGUE
Width 48"
Material: Fiberglas, Linen or 100% Fortisan
Designer and Manufacturer: Laverne Originals

Upper left
CONSTELLATION
Width 48/50″
Material: Hand-screened Vat Print. Cotton
Designer and Manufacturer: Cohama

Lower left
AZTEC CALENDAR
No. 1455
Width 50″
Material: Silk Warp, Jacquard Weave
Designer: Franco Scalamandré
Manufacturer: Scalamandré Silks, Inc.

Lower right
ECLIPSE
Width 48″
Material: Cotton Velvet, Linen or Quilted Linen
Designer: Warren Platner
Manufacturer: Jack Lenor Larsen, Inc.

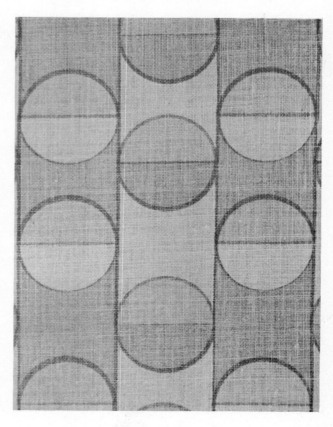

Upper left
SPACIAL
Width 50"
Material: Hand Print on Linen
Designer: Louise Shiffer
Manufacturer: Isabel Scott Fabrics Corporation

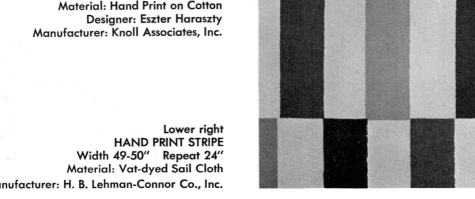

Upper right
KNOLL STRIPES
Width 50"
Material: Hand Print on Cotton
Designer: Eszter Haraszty
Manufacturer: Knoll Associates, Inc.

Lower right
HAND PRINT STRIPE
Width 49-50"   Repeat 24"
Material: Vat-dyed Sail Cloth
Designer and Manufacturer: H. B. Lehman-Connor Co., Inc.

Upper left
ASTARTE
No. 9110
Width 54"
Material: Silk and Bemberg
Designer: Boris Kroll
Manufacturer: Boris Kroll Fabrics, Inc.

Upper right
MALIBU DRIFTWOOD
Width 50"   Repeat 24"
Material: Hand-screened Fabric. All Cotton
Designer: Dorie March
Manufacturer: Schiffer Prints Division, Mil-Art Co., Inc.

Lower left
TAMBU TEXTURE H. P.
No. 21825 Series
Width 48"
Material: Rayon, Cotton and Mohair
Designer and Manufacturer: J. H. Thorp & Co., Inc.

MODERNA
Width 50″   Repeat 10″
Material: Hand Print on Linen
Designer and Manufacturer: H. B. Lehman-Connor Co., Inc.

VENERABLE SIR
No. 6440
Width 45″   Repeat 28″
Material: Rayon-backed Linen
Styled by Maggie Miklas
Manufacturer: Edwin Raphael Company, Inc.

RIBBON
No. 83271
Width 50″
Material: Hand-printed Linen
Designer: Arne Jacobsen
For Stroheim & Romann

POPLARS
Width 48"   Repeat 12"
Material: Linen
Designer: Harvey Jason
Manufacturer: Konwiser, Inc.

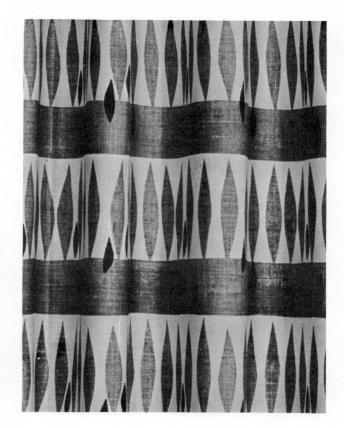

ARCHWAY
Width 48"   Repeat 18½"
Material: Flair Fortisan
Designer: Harvey Jason
Manufacturer: Konwiser, Inc.

KINGS KROWNS
No. 6090
Width 51"   Repeat 17½"
Material: Rayon-backed Linen
Designer: Dave Zeese
Manufacturer: Edwin Raphael Company, Inc.

309

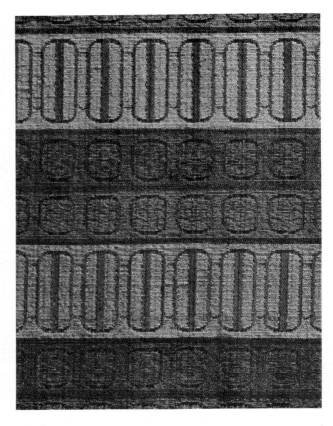

Upper left
CALLIGRAPHY
No. 50,000
Width 50"
Material: Imported Batiste
Designer: Boris Kroll
Manufacturer: Boris Kroll Fabrics, Inc.

Upper right
MONTE CARLO
No. 9909
Width 54"
Material: Viscose and Bemberg
Designer: Boris Kroll
Manufacturer: Boris Kroll Fabrics, Inc.

Lower right
ECLIPSE
No. 62040-43
Width 50"
Material: Hand-printed on White Fiberglas Sheer
Designer and Manufacturer: Cheney, Greeff & Co., Inc.

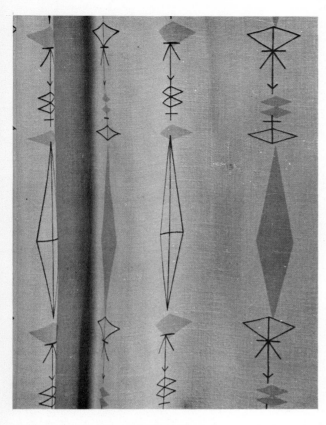

Upper left
RHOMBUS
No. 5504
Width 50"   Repeat 12"
Material: Imported Linen
Designer: Paul McCobb
Manufacturer: L. Anton Maix

Lower left
FLOATING JEWELS
No. 33640-33646
Width 53/54"
Material: Hand-printed 100% Cotton Imported Batiste
Designer and Manufacturer: S. M. Hexter Co.

Lower right
CURTAIN CALL
No. 6170
Width 51"   Repeat 35"
Material: Rayon-backed Linen
Designer: Dave Zeese
Manufacturer: Edwin Raphael Company, Inc.

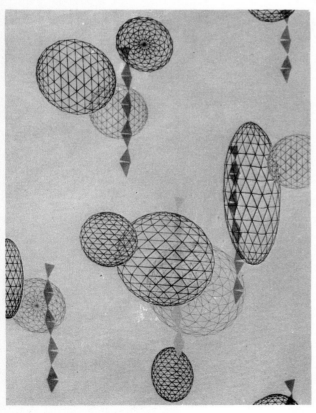

Upper right
IN HARMONY
Width 50"   Repeat 30½"
Material: Hand-screened Fabric. All Cotton
Designer: Tatsuhiko Heima
Manufacutrer: Schiffer Prints Division, Mil-Art Co.

Lower left
STELLA D'ORO
No. R-1312
Width 48"   Repeat 10½"
Material: 100% Cotton
Designer and Manufacturer: Riverdale Drapery Fabrics

Lower right
CATTAILS
No. 83310
Width 50"   Repeat 19½"
Material: Hand Print on Imported All Cotton
Designer: Arne Jacobsen
For Stroheim & Romann

Upper left
PHARAOH ABSTRACT H. P.
No. 20140
Width 50"
Material: 100% Dynel
Designer and Manufacturer: J. H. Thorp & Co., Inc.

Lower left
AFTER SHOWERS
Material: Silk Screen. Custom Printed
Designer: Julian Brogelton
Manufacturer: Isabel Scott Fabrics Corporation

Lower right
SPEARHEAD
Width 48"   Repeat 36"
Material: Flair Fortisan
Designer: Harvey Jason
Manufacturer: Konwiser, Inc.

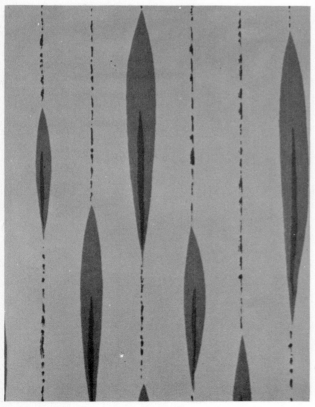

Upper right
SQUARE DANCE
No. R-1165
Width 48"   Repeat 11¼"
Material: 100% Cotton
Designer and Manufacturer: Riverdale Drapery Fabrics

Lower left
ATOMICS
Width 51"   Repeat 31"
Material: Linen
Designer: The Svedberg
For Bonniers

Lower right
MIKADO
No. 650
Width 48"   Repeat 12"
Material: Silk Gauze
Designer: Alexander Girard
Manufacturer: Herman Miller Fabrics

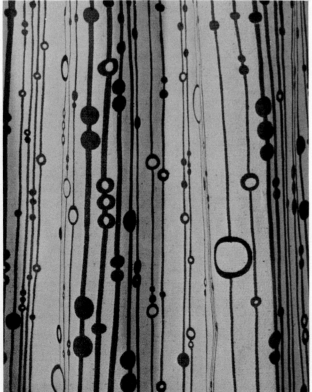

Upper left
BLOCK ISLAND
No. 33657-33660
Width 50"
Material: Hand-printed on 100% Cotton
Designer and Manufacturer: S. M. Hexter Co.

Upper right
THE SIAMESE BALLET
Width 50"   Repeat 28½"
Material: Hand-screened Fabric
Designer: Edward Daly Brown
Manufacturer: Schiffer Prints Division, Mil-Art Company, Inc.

Lower left
STRINGS AND THINGS
Width 54"   Repeat 29"
Material: Nubbin
Designer: Ruth Adler
Manufacturer: Adler-Schnee Associates

Upper right
SPELUNKING
No. 6160
Width 51"   Repeat 9½"
Material: Rayon-backed Linen
Designer: Pipsan Saarinen Swanson
Manufacturer: Edwin Raphael Company, Inc.

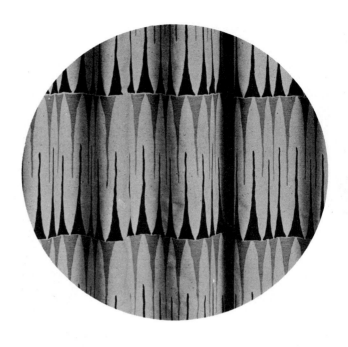

Lower left
FOOTHILLS
No. 6240
Width 51"   Repeat 20"
Material: Rayon-backed Linen
Designer: Harry Carpenter
Manufacturer: Edwin Raphael Company, Inc.

Lower right
RELATIVITY
No. 1074
Width 48"   Repeat 12"
Material: Linen or Suedetex
Designer and Manufacturer: Ben Rose

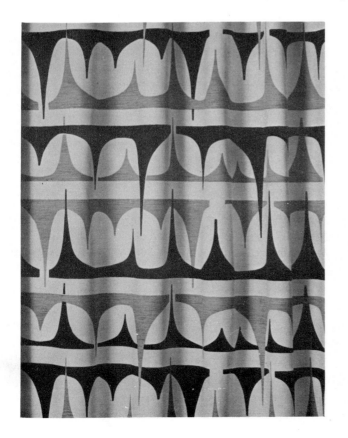

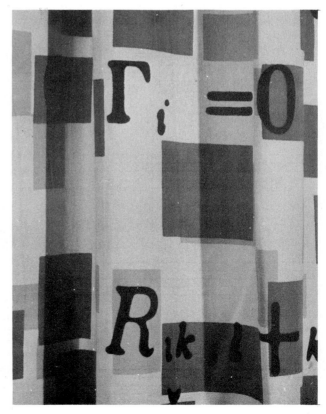

Upper left
TURNABOUT
No. 6450
Width 51″   Repeat 24¾″
Material: Rayon-backed Linen
Designer: Pipsan Saarinen Swanson
Manufacturer: Edwin Raphael Company, Inc.

Lower left
SCROMBER
No. 6030
Width 51″   Repeat 24″
Material: Rayon-backed Linen
Designer: Pipsan Saarinen Swanson
Manufacturer: Edwin Raphael Company, Inc.

Lower right
ROMAN NUMERALS
No. 1054
Width 48″   Repeat 6¾″
Material: Linen
Designer and Manufacturer: Ben Rose

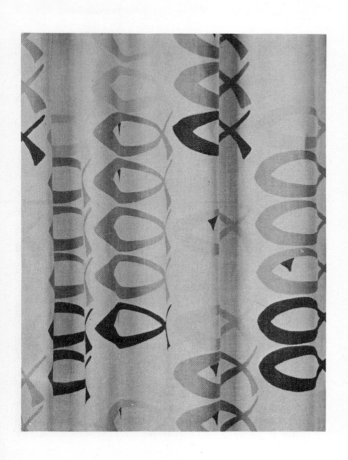

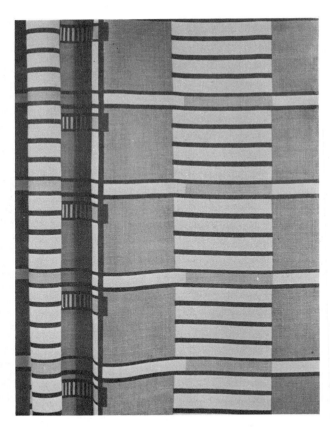

Upper left
TULIP TIME
No. 6300
Width 51"   Repeat 32"
Material: Rayon-backed Linen
Designer: Dave Zeese
Manufacturer: Edwin Raphael Company, Inc.

Upper right
FACADE
No. 5502
Width 50"   Repeat 4¾"
Material: Imported Linen
Designer: Joseph Baker
Manufacturer: L. Anton Maix

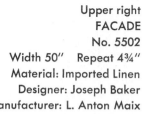

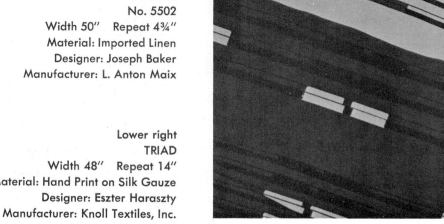

Lower right
TRIAD
Width 48"   Repeat 14"
Material: Hand Print on Silk Gauze
Designer: Eszter Haraszty
Manufacturer: Knoll Textiles, Inc.

Upper left
ADOBE HILLS
No. 5511
Width 50"   Repeat 9"
Material: Imported Linen
Designer: Jens Risom
Manufacturer: L. Anton Maix

Upper right
GROVES
No. 1072
Width 48"   Repeat 16"
Material: Randomweave, Opaque Fiberglas,
    Boucle Fiberglas, Linen Casement or
    Medium Weight Linen
Designer and Manufacturer: Ben Rose

Lower left
CHIPS
Width 50"   Repeat 27½"
Material: Hand-screened Fabric
Designer: George Nelson
Manufacturer: Schiffer Prints Division, Mil-Art Company, Inc.

319

FUGITIVE STRIPE
Width 50"   Repeat 27"
Material: Hand-screened Fabric
Designer: Edward J Wormley
Manufacturer: Schiffer Prints Division, Mil-Art Company, Inc.

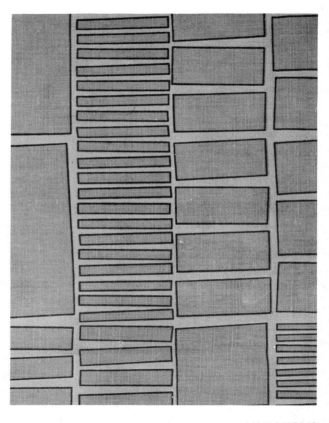

VARIATIONS
Material: One-color Print on Sheer Fabric
Designer: Angelo Testa
Manufacturer: Angelo Testa & Company

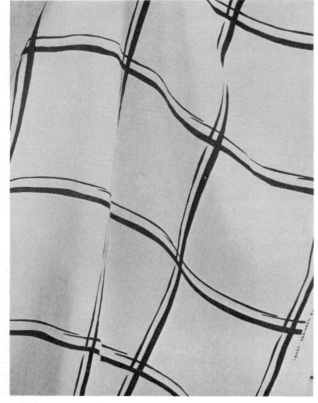

SHOGI
Width 50"   Repeat 12"
Material: Hand Print on Linen
Designer: Dennis Lennon
Manufacturer: Knoll Textiles, Inc.

PATHWAY
Width 48″   Repeat 24″
Material: Batiste
Designer: Sara Provan
Manufacturer: Konwiser, Inc.

LARGO
Width 48″   Repeat 28″
Material: Flanders Linen
Designer: Sara Provan
Manufacturer: Konwiser, Inc.

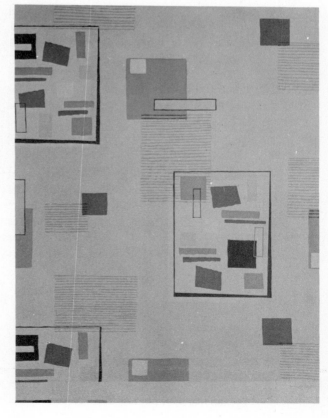

METROPOLIS
No. R-1278
Width 48″   Repeat 19½″
Material: 100% Cotton
Designer and Manufacturer: Riverdale Drapery Fabrics

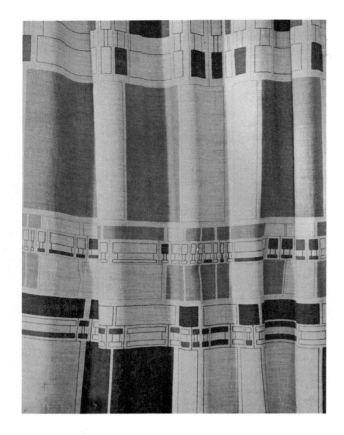

Upper left
BRICK-A-BLOCK
No. 2822
Repeat 31⅞"
Material: Available in 8 Fabrics
Designer: Ruth Adler
Manufacturer: Adler-Schnee Associates

Upper right
CONSTRUCTION
Repeat 29$\frac{7}{16}$"
Material: Available in 8 Fabrics
Designer: Ruth Adler
Manufacturer: Adler-Schnee Associates

Lower right
NEW DIMENSION
No. 33900-33906
Width 50"
Material: Hand-printed Sheer Linen Casement. 100% Linen
Designer and Manufacturer: S. M. Hexter Co.

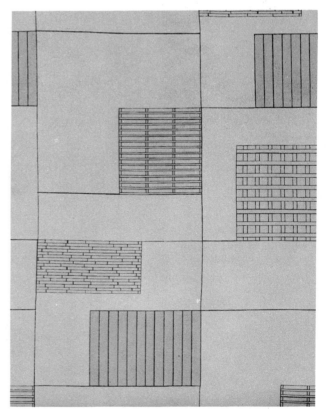

Upper left
FLUCTUATION
Width 48"   Repeat 5½"
Material: Fiberglas, Batiste, Linen
Designer and Manufacturer: Laverne Originals

Lower left
SI & NO
Width 50"   Repeat 27"
Material: Hand-screened Fabric
Designer: Bernard Rudofsky
Manufacturer: Schiffer Prints Division, Mil-Art Company, Inc.

Lower right
SUMMER RAIN
No. 6310
Width 45"   Repeat 24"
Designer: Dave Zeese
Manufacturer: Edwin Raphael Company, Inc.

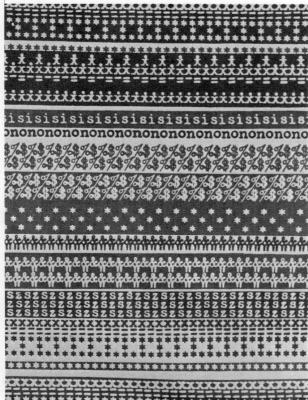

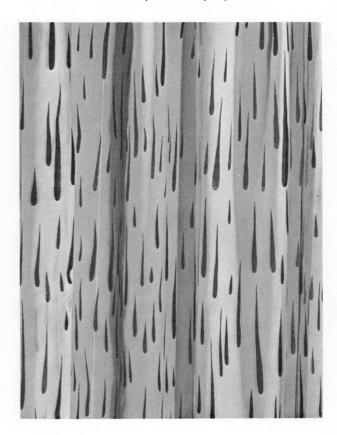

Upper right
DAI ICHI
No. 6320
Width 45"   Repeat 10"
Material: Orlon Silk Casement
Designer: Pipsan Saarinen Swanson
Manufacturer: Edwin Raphael Company, Inc.

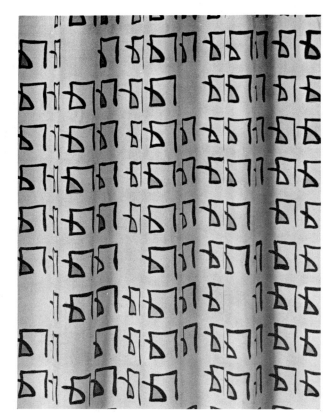

Lower left
CARIOCA
Width 48"
Material: Fiberglas, Batiste, Linen
Designer and Manufacturer: Laverne Originals

Lower right
PENMANSHIP
No. 5506
Width 50"   Repeat 12⅞"
Material: Imported Linen
Designer: Harold Leeds
Manufacturer: L. Anton Maix

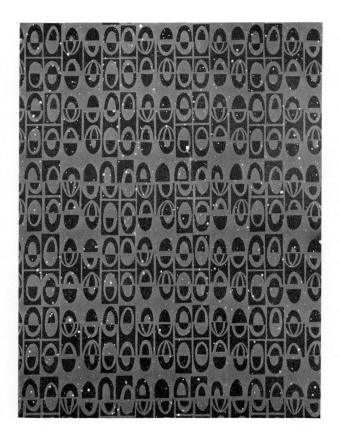

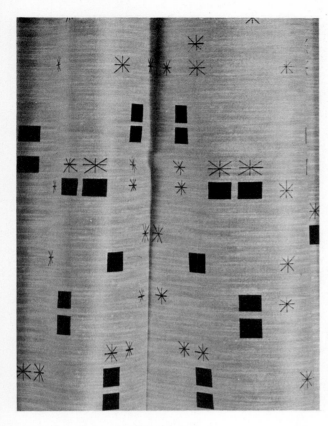

Upper left
CENTRAL PARK SOUTH
Repeat: 29⅝"
Material: Available in 8 Fabrics
Designer: Ruth Adler
Manufacturer: Adler-Schnee Associates

Lower left
PRELUDE
No. 5509
Width 50"　Repeat 27"
Material: Imported Linen
Designer: Erik Nitsche
Manufacturer: L. Anton Maix

Lower right
BROCADE
No. 135
Width 54"
Material: Spun Rayon, Cotton, Lurex
Designer: Alexander Girard
Manufacturer: Herman Miller Fabrics

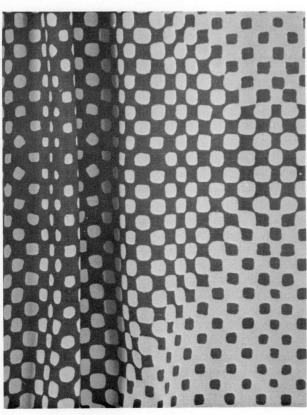

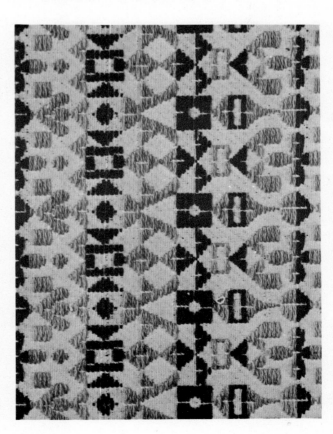

Upper right
HANO
No. 33550-33556
Width 48"
Material: Hand-printed on 100% Linen
Designer and Manufacturer: S. M. Hexter Co.

Lower left
LUSTRUM
Width 48"   Repeat 48"
Material: Sahara Cotton Rayon
Designer: Sara Provan
Manufacturer: Konwiser, Inc.

Lower right
FACADE
Material: Cotton, Batiste or Fiberglas
Designer: Angelo Testa
Manufacturer: Angelo Testa & Company

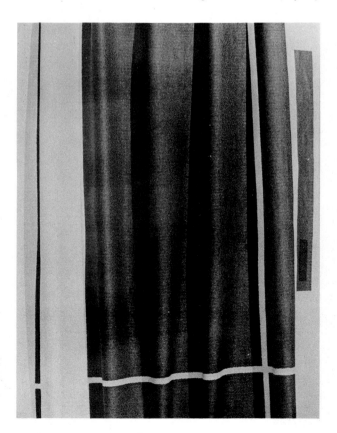

Upper left
CONSTRUCTION
No. 3151
Width 50"
Material: Jacquard Weave on Silk Warp
Designer: Gino Scalamandré
Manufacturer: Scalamandré Silks, Inc.

Upper right
ALGIERS
Material: Cotton, Batiste or Fiberglas
Designer: Angelo Testa
Manufacturer: Angelo Testa & Company

Lower left
APARTMENT HOUSE AT NIGHT
No. 1508
Width 50"
Material: Silk Warp. Jacquard Loom
Designer: Franco Scalamandré
Manufacturer: Scalamandré Silks, Inc.

Upper right
DESIGN 102
No. 8-8551
Width 50"   Repeat 28½"
Material: Printed Belgian Linen
Designer: Frank Lloyd Wright
Manufacturer: F. Schumacher & Co.

Lower left
TRELLIS
Width 36"   Repeat 2¾"
Material: Vat-dyed Sail Cloth
Designer and Manufacturer: H. B. Lehman-Connor Co., Inc.

Lower right
IMPORTED TAOS H. P.
No. 21905
Width 50"
Material: Cotton
Designer and Manufacturer: J. H. Thorp & Co., Inc.

Upper left
DESIGN 101
Width 50"   Repeat 29"
Material: Printed Belgian Linen
Designer: Frank Lloyd Wright
Manufacturer: F. Schumacher & Co.

Lower left
SUPERSTRIPE
No. 665
Width 48"
Material: Linen
Designer: Alexander Girard
Manufacturer: Herman Miller Fabrics

Lower right
LINES
Nos. 610-611
Width 48"
Material: Fine White Batiste or White Parma Linen
Designer: Alexander Girard
Manufacturer: Herman Miller Fabrics

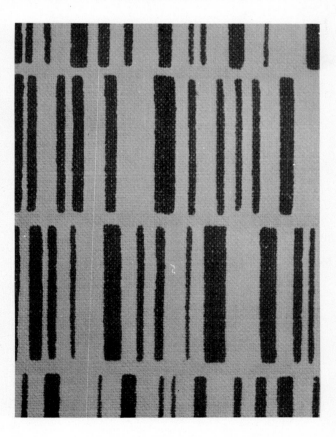

Upper left
BOTANIC
Repeat 25"
Material: Custom-printed in Any Colors on Choice of
Ground Fabrics
Designer and Manufacturer: Elenhank Designers

Upper right
CLAIRE DE LUNE
Width 50"   Repeat 29½"
Material: All Cotton Warp Sateen
Designer: Tatsuhiko Heima
Manufacturer: Schiffer Prints Division, Mil-Art Company, Inc.

Lower right
CONIFER
Material: Custom Hand-screened Print in 7-Foot or
9-Foot Height
Designer: Shirley St. John
Manufacturer: Jack Lenor Larsen

Upper left
PINEWOODS
No. 21838
Width 48"   Repeat 24"
Material: Cotton and Rayon
Designer and Manufacturer: J. H. Thorp & Co., Inc.

Upper right
FOREST
Repeat 26½"
Material: Custom-printed in Any Colors on Choice of
    Ground Fabrics
Designer and Manufacturer: Elenhank Designers

Lower left
SEEDY WEEDS
Repeat 29"
Material: Available in 6 fabrics
Designer: Ruth Adler
Manufacturer: Adler-Schnee Associates

VERSAILLES
Width 36"
Material: Polished Cotton
Designer and Manufacturer: Everfast Fabrics, Inc.

LEFT BANK
Width: 36"
Material: Polished Cotton
Designer and Manufacturer: Everfast Fabrics, Inc.

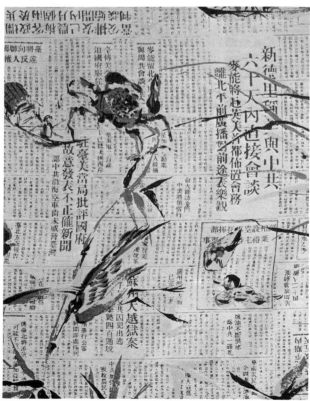

LOTUS
Width 48/50"   Repeat 34"
Material: Hand-screen Print. Fortisan and Rayon
Designer and Manufacturer: Cohama

SPHERE OF INFLUENCE
Width 50"   Repeat 27"
Material: Hand-screened Fabric
Designer: George Nelson
Manufacturer: Schiffer Prints Division, Mil-Art Company, Inc.

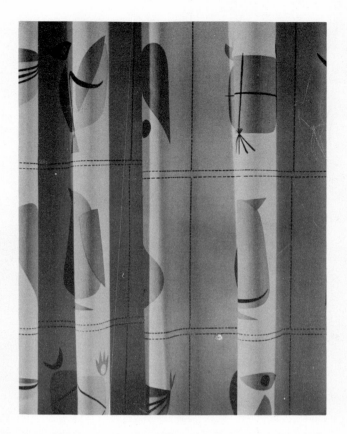

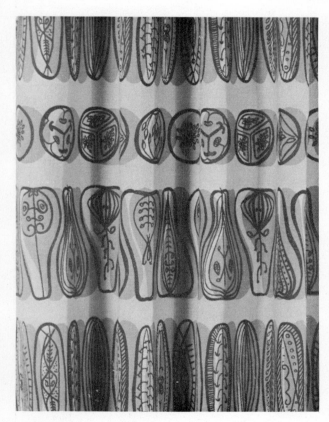

FRUIT ELEMENTS
No. 5508
Width 50"   Repeat 14½"
Material: Imported Linen
Designer: O. L. Baughman
Manufacturer: L. Anton Maix

CHINA SHOP
Width 50"   Repeat 13"
Material: Hand-screened Fabric
Designer: George Nelson
Manufacturer: Schiffer Prints Division, Mil-Art Company, Inc.

Upper left
NORSE MYTHOLOGY PANEL
Repeat 48"
Material: Custom-printed in Any Colors on Choice of
Ground Fabrics
Designer and Manufacturer: Elenhank Designers

Upper right
TROVATORI
Width 36"
Material: Polished Cotton
Designer and Manufacturer: Everfast Fabrics, Inc.

Lower right
POT LUCK
No. 5260
Width 35/36"
Material: All-cotton Everglaze Chintz
Designer and Manufacturer: Cyrus Clark Co., Inc.

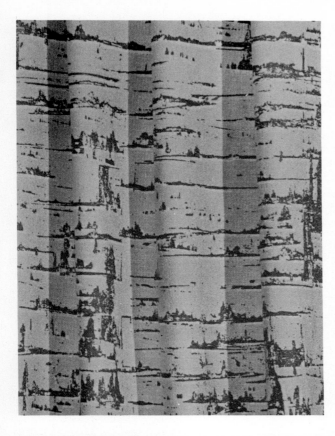

Upper left
VISTA
Width 48"
Material: Batiste
Designer: Sara Provan
Manufacturer: Konwiser, Inc.

Lower left
TRIANGLES
Nos. 560, 561
Width 48"
Material: Linen or Silk Gauze
Designer: Alexander Girard
Manufacturer: Herman Miller Fabrics

Lower right
KALEIDOSCOPE
No. 648
Width 48"   Repeat 24"
Material: Fortisan, Poplin, Chintz
Designer: Alexander Girard
Manufacturer: Herman Miller Fabrics

Upper right
TANG HORSES
Width 50"   Repeat 30"
Material: Fortisan and Rayon
Designer: Baker Davis
Manufacturer: Erbun Fabrics Corporation

Lower left
ETUDE
Width 48"
Material: Hand-printed Bemberg and Fortisan Sheer
Designer and Manufacturer: Cheney, Greeff & Co., Inc.

Lower right
PRINTING PRESSES
Repeat 32"
Material: Custom-printed in Any Colors on Choice of
Ground Fabrics
Designer and Manufacturer: Elenhank Designers

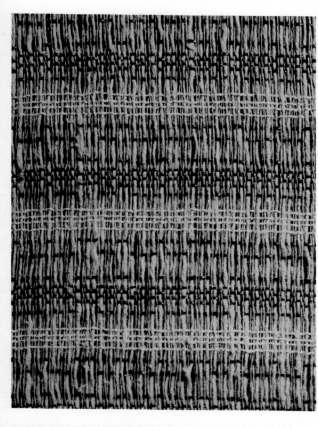

Upper left
TANGLEWOOD
No. 600Z
Width 50"
Material: Linen and Cotton Texture Casement
Designer and Manufacturer: Isabel Scott Fabrics Corporation

Lower left
DEL RIO
Width 50"   Repeat 15"
Material: Linen and Rayon
Designer and Manufacturer: H. B. Lehman-Connor Co., Inc.

Lower right
LINO SHEER
Width 50"
Material: Linen, Spun Rayon, Hemp
Designer: Hugo Dreyfuss
Manufacturer: Kagan-Dreyfuss, Inc.

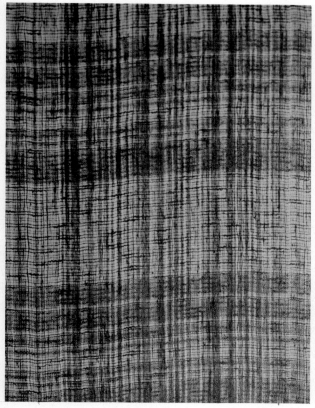

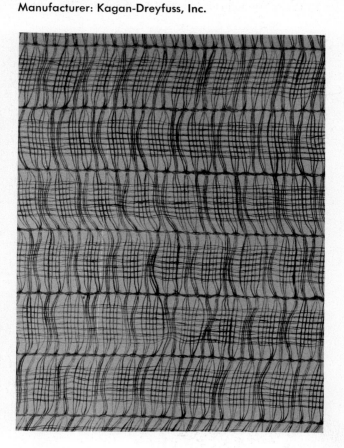

Upper right
SUPERSPUN
Width 50″ Repeat 6″
Material: Linen, Cotton
Designer: Hugo Dreyfuss
Manufacturer: Kagan-Dreyfuss, Inc.

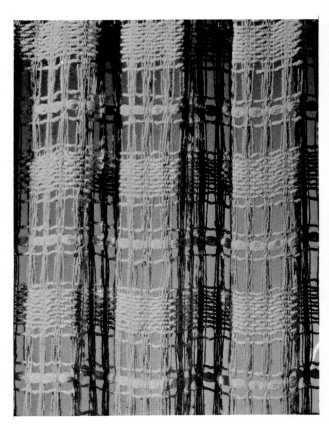

Lower left
FIBRA
Width 50″ Repeat 36″
Material: Belgian Linen
Designer: Eszter Harszty
Manufacturer: Knoll Textiles, Inc.

Lower right
STRIPLING
No. 607
Width 50″
Material: Open Weave Linen and Cotton Threads
Designer and Manufacturer: Isabel Scott Fabrics Corporation

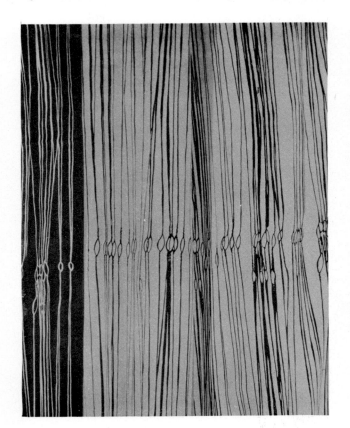

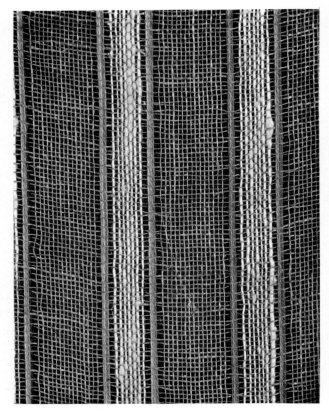

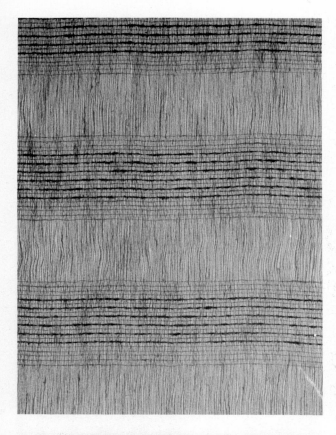

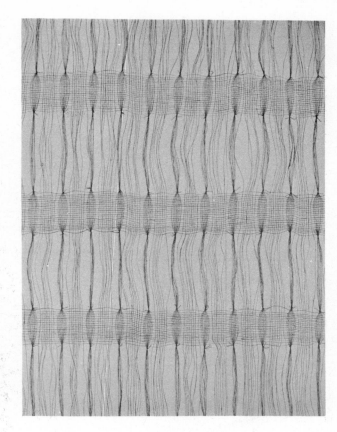

Upper left
PRISTINE
Width 50"
Material: Ramie and Raw Silk Threads
Designer and Manufacturer: Isabel Scott Fabrics Corporation

Upper right
FISHERMAN'S LUCK
Width 20"
Material: Linen Fish Line
Designer and Manufacturer: Isabel Scott Fabrics Corporation

Lower left
HEAVY SILK TEXTURE
Material: Knubby on Cotton Warp
Designer: Gino Scalamandré
Manufacturer: Scalamandré Silks, Inc.

LUXARTEX
Width 50″
Material: Hemp, Cotton, Rayon and Lurex
Designer: Hugo Dreyfuss
Manufacturer: Kagan-Dreyfuss, Inc.

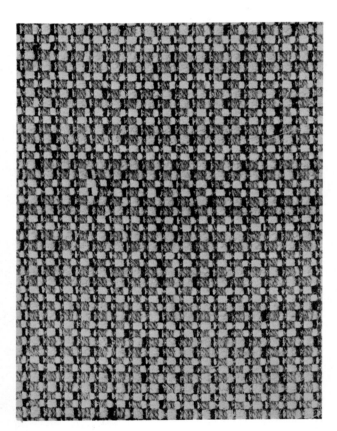

MONACO
Width 54″
Material: Wool, Cotton, Rayon
Designer: Lyda Weyl
Manufacturer: Konwiser, Inc.

CONFERENCE
No. 92930-31
Width 52″
Material: Linen, Rayon and Lurex
Designer and Manufacturer: Cheney, Greeff & Co., Inc.

THORPE WEAVE
Width 54"
Material: Wool, Cotton, Rayon
Designer: Azalea S. Thorpe
Manufacturer: Konwiser, Inc.

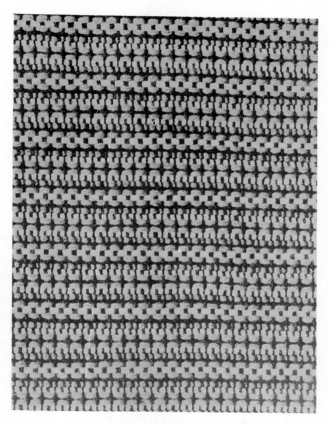

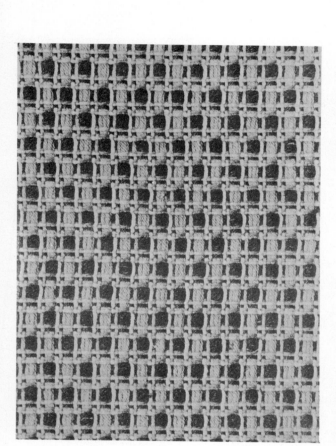

BAHIA
Width 54"
Material: Cotton, Wool
Designer: Lyda Weyl
Manufacturer: Konwiser, Inc.

WOVEN MATERIAL
Width 50"
Designer: Dorothy Liebes
For Dorothy Liebes Textiles Inc.

ANDCARPETSRUGSANDCARPETSRUGSANDCARPETSRUGSANDCARPETSRUGSANDCARPETSRUGSAN
ANDCARPETSRUGSANDCARPETSRUGSANDCARPETSRUGSANDCARPETSRUGSANDCARPETSRUGSAN
ANDCARPETSRUGSANDCARPETSRUGSANDCARPETSRUGSANDCARPETSRUGSANDCARPETSRUGSAN
ANDCARPETSRUGSANDCARPETSRUGSANDCARPETSRUGSANDCARPETSRUGSANDCARPETSRUGSAN
ANDCARPETSRUGSANDCARPETSRUGSANDCARPETSRUGSANDCARPETSRUGSANDCARPETSRUGSAN
ANDCARPETSRUGSANDCARPETSRUGSANDCARPETSRUGSANDCARPETSRUGSANDCARPETSRUGSAN
ANDCARPETSRUGSANDCARPETSRUGSANDCARPETSRUGSANDCARPETSRUGSANDCARPETSRUGSAN

Hand-hooked rug
BAS RELIEF
Size 6' x 9'
Material: Wool
Colors: Red Orange, Putty White, Slate, Khaki-Black-White,
    Blue Green, Camel Beige
Designer: Warren Platner
For Jack Lenor Larsen Inc.

Basketweave Carpet
MARK 90
Widths 9′, 12′ and 15′
Material: All-wool Face
Colors: Rock Grey, Hampton Beige, Sutter Gold,
Corsage Green
Designer and Manufacturer: C. H. Masland & Sons

Velvet-weave Carpet
GULISTAN DOCUMENT
Widths 9′, 12′ and 15′
Material: All Wool
Colors: Alabaster Beige, Malayan Mocha, Glen Green,
Nutria Nuance, Antique Silver, Sandalwood Glow
Designer and Manufacturer: A. & M. Karagheusian

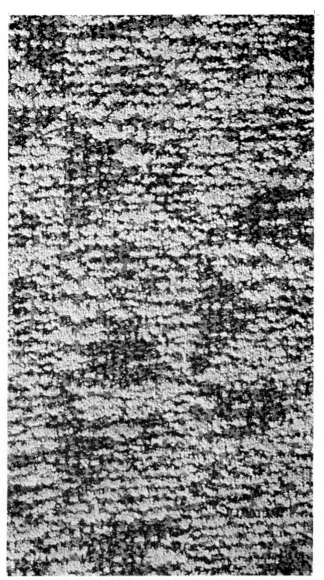

Two-level, Two-tone Carpet
BARCELONA
Widths 9', 12' and 15'
Colors: Beige, Spice, Grey, Green
Designer and Manufacturer: Sanford Carpets

Three-level Pile Carpet
MONTE CARLO
Widths up to 15'
Material: Wool with Plasticized Metallic Gold Threads
Designer and Manufacturer: Bigelow Rugs and Carpets

Looped-pile Carpet
GULISTAN MARBURY
Widths 27″, 9′, 12′ and 15′
Material: All Wool
Colors: Combinations of Beige, Mocha, Green, Grey and
    Sandalwood
Designer and Manufacturer: A. & M. Karagheusian

Textured Carpet
IRIDESCENT
Widths to 15′
Material: All Wool
Colors: Sea Green with Shell Beige, Beach Woods with
    Sand Beige
Designer and Manufacturer: James Lees and Sons Company

Textured Carpet
VIRGINIAN
Widths up to 12'
Material: All Wool
Colors: Amethyst Beige with Accents of Ruby,
    Turquoise, Aqua
Designer and Manufacturer: James Lees and Sons Company

Two-level Pile Carpet
THE BARBERRY COAST
Widths 9', 12' and 15'
Material: Wool with Gold Metallic Thread.
Colors: Three Colorings: Green, Grey, Nutria
Designer and Manufacturer: Sanford Carpets

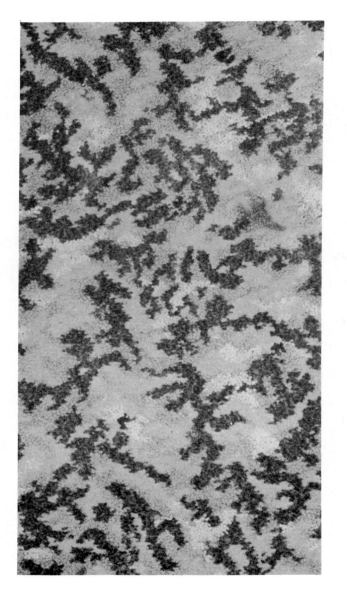
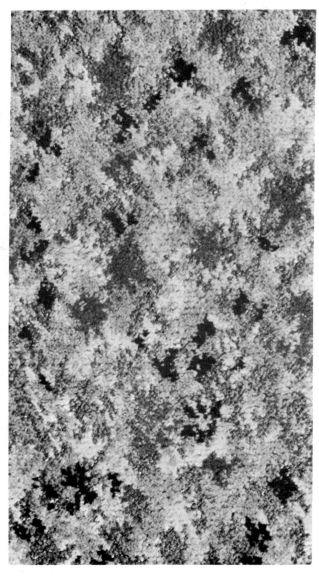

Two-toned Stripe Rug
CAMPANIA
Sizes 2'3" x 4' to 9' x 12'
Material: Cotton and Rayon
Colors: Gold, Cantaloupe and White; Emerald, Black and
White; Grey, Black and White; Brown, Black and White;
Brown, Beige and Natural
Designer and Manufacturer:
Needletuft Rug Mills, Floor Covering Division of Cabin Crafts

Centerpoint Rug
ROOSTER & ROSES
Sizes 6' x 9', 9' x 12'
Material: All Wool
Colors: Turquoise, Black and Moroccan White on
    Cinnamon Background
Designer: Emma and Thomas Elsner
Manufacturer: Alexander Smith

350

Rug
SUN DANCE
Sizes 6' x 9', 9' x 12'
Material: All Wool
Colors: Moroccan White, Two Values of Grey Blue, Two Values
of Avocado, Pale Tawny Beige on White and Plum Ground
Designer: Lamartine Le Goullon
Manufacturer: Alexander Smith

Basketweave Carpet
RIPPLETONE
Widths 9', 12' and 15'
Material: Wool
Colors: Icelandic Green; South Sea Coral; Rock Grey;
Golden Sand; Tree Bark; Forest Floor; Salon Beige,
Mist Grey, Corsage Green
Designer and Manufacturer: C. H. Masland and Sons

Two-level Carpet
BEAUVAIS
Widths: 9', 12' and 15'
Material: Wool
Colors: Cocoa to Beige with Flecks of Coral, Green,
    Ivory, Chocolate
Designer and Manufacturer: Bigelow Rugs and Carpets

Gold-flecked Carpet
THE FORTY-NINER
Widths 9', 12' and 15'
Material: Wool
Colors: Beige, Grey, Nutria, Green
Designer and Manufacturer: Sanford Carpets

Sculptured Carpet
GULISTAN PALAIS ROYAL
Widths 9' and 12'
Material: Wool
Colors: Aqua; Rose; Light Beige and Dark Beige Backgrounds
Designer and Manufacturer: A. & M. Karagheusian

Diamond-pattern Rug
PIERROT
Sizes 2'3" x 4' to 9' x 12'
Material: Rayon and Cotton
Colors: Black and White; Red and Black; Grey and Pink;
   Black and Grey; Black and Aqua; Brown and Palm;
   Brown and Toast
Designer and Manufacturer: Needletuft Rug Mills,
   Floor Covering Division of Cabin Crafts

Danish Rug
UNIKACARPET
Size 5'8" x 7'6"
Material: Wool
Colors: Reds or Blues
Designer: Nanna and Jorgen Ditzel
For George Tanier, Inc.

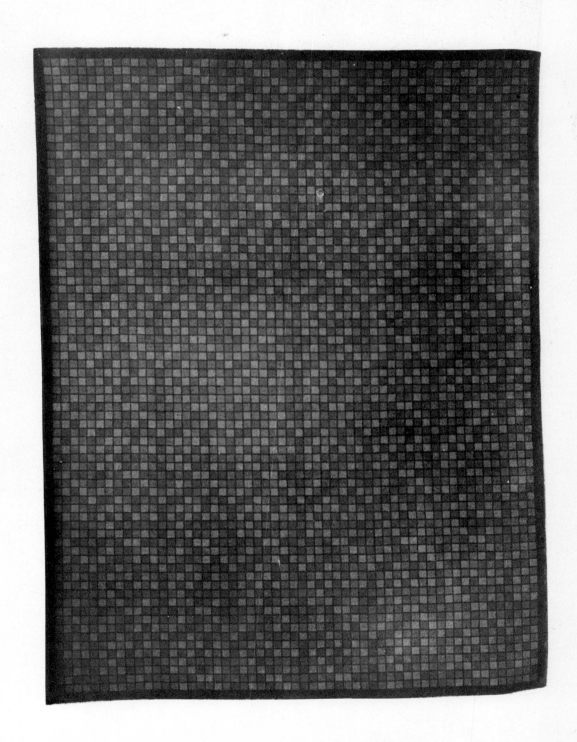

Area Rug
DESERT STAR
Size 6' x 9'
Material: Wool
Colors: Gold Background, Green Stars, Red Dots
Designer and Manufacturer: Karastan

Area Rug
MANDARIN
Sizes 4'6" x 6' to 15' x 24'
Material: Wool
Colors: Available in 16 Colors
Designer and Manufacturer: Karastan

Area Rug
JAPANESE CLOUD
Sizes 4'6" x 6' to 15' x 24'
Material: Wool
Colors: Available in 16 Colors
Designer and Manuacturer: Karastan

Area Rug
HELLENIC
Sizes 4'6" x 6' to 15' x 24'
Material: Wool
Colors: Available in 16 Colors
Designer and Manufacturer: Karastan

Area Rug
PLAID
Sizes 4'6" x 6' to 15' x 24'
Material: Wool
Colors: Available in 16 Colors
Designer and Manufacturer: Karastan

Sunburst Design Rug
CLASSIC FLAIR
Sizes 6' x 9' and 9' x 12'
Material: Wool
Colors: Brassy Gold, Light Gold, Grey, Brown on Grey
Background; Cool Turquoise, Blue, Violet on Grey and
Blue Background
Designer: William Ward Beecher
Manufacturer: Alexander Smith

Accent Rug
FUTURA
Sizes: 2'3" x 4' to 9' x 12'
Material: Rayon with Gold Metallic Threads
Colors: Toast and Butterscotch; Canary and Brass;
Natural and Rose; Natural and Palm Green;
Turquoise and Tangier White
Designer and Manufacturer:
Needletuft Rug Mills, Floor Covering Division of Cabin Crafts

Area Rug
NIGHT FLOWERS
Size 6' x 9'
Material: Wool
Colors: Charcoal Background with Flowers in Brilliant Colors
Designer and Manufacturer: Karastan

MANUFACTURERS AND REPRESENTATIVES

Adler-Schnee Associates, 16805 Livernois Avenue, Detroit 21, Michigan

Altamira, 18 East 50 Street, New York 22, New York

Arredoluce, Milan, Italy

Avard, 66 West 55 Street, New York 19, New York

Baker Furniture, Inc., Grand Rapids 2, Michigan

Bay & Co., Milan, Italy

Willy Beck, Snedkermester Classensgade 25A, Copenhagen, Denmark

V Bega & Figli, Bolona, Italy

Bell & Howell Company, 7100 McCormack Road, Chicago 45, Illinois

Berge-Norman Associates, Inc., 1 Park Avenue, New York 16, New York

Bigelow Rugs and Carpets, 140 Madison Avenue, New York, New York

Bonniers, 605 Madison Avenue, New York, New York

Rene Brancusi Co., Inc., 1001 First Avenue, New York, New York

The Brandt Cabinet Works, Inc., Hagerstown, Maryland

Cabin Crafts, Incorporated, 7 East 35 Street, New York 16, New York

Calvin Furniture Company, 1000 - 36th Street S.E., Grand Rapids,
Michigan

Charak Furniture Company, 444 Madison Avenue, New York,
New York

Cheney, Greeff & Company, Inc., 150 Midland Avenue, Portchester,
New York

Cyrus Clark Company, Inc., 267 Fifth Avenue, New York, New York

Cohama, 214 Madison Avenue, New York 16, New York

Colby Associates, 239 East 27 Street, New York, New York

Custom Craft, Inc., 1923 S. Halsted Street, Chicago, Illinois

Figli di Amedeo, Milan, Italy

Directional Manufacturing Company, 201 East 57 Street, New York,
New York

Drexel Furniture Company, Drexel, North Carolina

Dunbar Furniture Corporation of Indiana, Berne, Indiana

Dux Incorporated, 390 Ninth Street, San Francisco, California

Dwight Furniture Company, 28 Ionia Avenue S.W., Grand Rapids,
Michigan

MANUFACTURERS AND REPRESENTATIVES
(continued)

Edgewood Furniture Company, Inc., 208 East 27 Street, New York, New York

Elenhank Designers, 5715 South Ada Street, Chicago, Illinois

Erbun Fabrics Corporation, 19 East 21 Street, New York, New York

Erwin-Lambeth, Inc., 136 East 40 Street, New York, New York

Everfast Fabrics, Inc., 70 West 40 Street, New York, New York

Excelsior Art Studios, 18 West 18 Street, New York, New York

Ficks-Reed Company, 424 Findlay Street, Cincinnati 4, Ohio

Finland House, 41 East 50 Street, New York, New York

General Lighting Company, 248 McKibbin Street, Brooklyn 6, New York

Glenn of California, 130 North First Avenue, Box 676, Arcadia, California

Allan Gould Designs, Inc., 166 Lexington Avenue, New York, New York

Habitat, 235 East 58 Street, New York, New York

Hansen, 978 First Avenue, New York, New York

Fritz Hansens, Dronningensgade 3, Copenhagen, Denmark

Heritage Henredon, High Point, North Carolina

S. M. Hexter Company, 509 Madison Avenue, New York, New York

Imperial Furniture Company, Grand Rapids, Michigan

j g Furniture Company, 543 Madison Avenue, New York, New York

Kagan-Dreyfuss, Inc., 125 East 57 Street, New York, New York

A. and M. Karagheusian, 295 Fifth Avenue, New York, New York

Karastan, 295 Fifth Avenue, New York, New York

Knoll Associates, Inc., 575 Madison Avenue, New York, New York

Knoll Textiles, Inc., 575 Madison Avenue, New York, New York

Koch & Lowy Mfg. Co., 201 East 34 Street, New York, New York

Konwiser, Inc., 1 East 53 Street, New York, New York

Boris Kroll Fabrics, Inc., 220 East 51 Street, New York, New York

La Riviere, Inc., 4101 East Eleventh Avenue, Hialeah, Florida

Jack Lenor Larsen, Inc., 36 East 22 Street, New York, New York

Leslie Larson, 56 East 66 Street, New York, New York

Laverne Originals, 160 East 57 Street, New York, New York

James Lees & Sons Company, 295 Fifth Avenue, New York, New York

H. B. Lehman-Connor Company, Inc., 500 Madison Avenue, New York, New York

Dorothy Liebes Textiles, 305 East 63 Street, New York, New York

Lightolier, Inc., 11 East 36 Street, New York, New York

L. Anton Maix, 162 East 59 Street, New York, New York

Marden Mfg. Inc., 1015 No. Halsted Street, Chicago, Illinois

C. H. Masland & Sons, 295 Fifth Avenue, New York, New York

The McGuire Company, 38 Hotaling Place, San Francisco, California

Middletown Manufacturing Company, 200 Monhagen Avenue, Middletown, New York

Herman Miller Fabrics, Zeeland, Michigan

Herman Miller Furniture Company, Zeeland, Michigan

Murray Furniture Manufacturing Company, Winchendon, Massachusetts

Nassjo Stolfabrik, Sweden

Nessen Studio, Inc., 5 University Place, New York, New York

Pacific Overseas, Inc., Jackson Square, San Francisco, California

Parzinger Originals, Inc., 301 East 55 Street, New York, New York

Charles Pechanec, Jr., 35 North Craig Avenue, Pasadena, California

Harvey Probber, Inc., 136 Fifth Avenue, New York, New York

Edwin Raphael Company, Inc., 157 Central Avenue, Holland, Michigan

Raymor, 225 Fifth Avenue, New York, New York

Rembrandt Lamp Corp. (Colonial-Premier Division), Rembrandt Building, Chicago, Illinois

Jens Risom Design, Inc., 59 East 53 Street, New York, New York

Riverdale Drapery Fabrics, 261 Fifth Avenue, New York, New York

Edward Axel Roffman Associates, Inc., 17 East 48 Street, New York, New York

Romweber, Batesville, Indiana

Ben Rose, 1129 West Sheridan Road, Chicago, Illinois

H. Sacks & Sons, 155 Harvard Street, Brookline, Massachusetts

John B. Salterini Co., Inc., 510 East 72 Street, New York, New York

Sanford Carpets, 295 Fifth Avenue, New York, New York

Scalamandré Silks, Inc., 37-24 - 24th Street, Long Island City, New York

Schiffer Prints Division, Mil-Art Company, Inc., 79 Madison Avenue, New York, New York

F. Schumacher & Company, 60 West 40 Street, New York, New York

Isabel Scott Fabrics Corporation, 515 Madison Avenue, New York, New York

Selig Manufacturing Company, Inc., Leominster, Massachusetts

M. Singer & Sons, 36 East 19 Street, New York, New York

Sligh Furniture, 1661 Monroe N.W., Grand Rapids, Michigan

Smilow-Thielle, 865 Lexington Avenue, New York, New York

Alexander Smith, Inc., 295 Fifth Avenue, New York, New York

Soborg Mobelfabrik, Soborg, Denmark

Stamford, 429 West Broadway, New York, New York

Statton Furniture Manufacturing Company, Hagerstown, Maryland

Stroheim & Romann, 35 East 53 Street, New York, New York

Sydney Chairs, Inc., Detroit, Michigan

George Tanier, Inc., 521 Madison Avenue, New York, New York

Tecno, Italy

Angelo Testa & Co., 49 East Ontario Street, Chicago, Illinois

J. H. Thorp & Co., Inc., 250 Park Avenue, New York, New York

Furniture by Tomlinson, High Point, North Carolina

Valley Upholstery Corporation, 428 West 14 Street, New York, New York

Van Keppel-Green, 9501 Santa Monica Boulevard, Beverly Hills, California

Paolo Venini, Venice, Italy

Kurt Versen Company, Englewood, New Jersey

Vista Furniture Company, 1040 North Olive, Anaheim, California

The Widdicomb Furniture Company, 514 Fifth Street, Grand Rapids 2, Michigan

Winchendon Furniture Company, Winchendon, Massachusetts

Lee L. Woodard Sons, 305 East 63 Street, New York, New York

DESIGNERS

Ruth Adler
Bengt Akerblom
William Armbruster
Joseph Baker
Robert Balonick
D. R. Bates
Milo Baughman
O. L. Baughman
William L. Beard
William Ward Beecher
Marc Berge
Helge Bibast
Julian Brogelton
Edward Daly Brown
Lewis Butler
Harry Carpenter
S. Chermayeff
Warner R. Cleveland
Paul Colby
Baker Davis
Carlo De Carli
Morris de la Cerda
Freda Diamond
Nanna and Jorgen Ditzel
Hugo Dreyfuss
Charles Eames
Emma and Thomas Elsner
Carl Fagerlund
Barney Flagg
Eleanor Forbes
Bertil Fridhagen
Alexander Girard
Harry Gitlin

Rex Goode
Allan Gould
Taylor Green
Jackson Gregory, Jr.
Greta Grossman
Harry Handler
Eszter Haraszty
Tatsuhiko Heima
Heritage Design Department
Arne Hiorth
Lorin Jackson
Arne Jacobsen
Harvey Jason
Finn Juhl
Vladimir Kagan
Richard Kelly
Florence Knoll
Knoll Planning Unit
Donn Knorr
IB Kofod-Larsen
Osten Kristiansson
Boris Kroll
Darrell Landrum
Marcel La Riviere
Ejner Larsen
Leslie Larson
Harold Leeds
Lamartine Le Goullon
Dennis Lennon
Dorothy Liebes
Ernest Lowy
Stewart MacDougall
Norman Fox MacGregor

A. Bender Madsen
    and Schubell
Dorie March
Sven Markelius
Paul Mayen
Paul McCobb Design
    Associates
John C. McGuire
George Mergenov
Maggie Miklas
Borge Mogensen
Thomas Moser
George Nelson
M. Lila Neuss
Erik Nitsche
Isamu Noguchi
Folke Ohlsson
Ico Parisi
Tommi Parzinger
Charles Pechanec, Jr.
Martin Perfit
J. Gordon Perlmutter
Warren Platner
Gio Ponti
Harvey Probber
Sara Provan
Jens Risom
T. H. Robsjohn-Gibbings
Edward A. Roffman
Bernard Rudofsky
Eero Saarinen
Shirley St. John
Adriana Scalamandré

DESIGNERS (continued)

Franco Scalamandré
Gino Scalamandré
Bertha Schaefer
Richard Schultz
Harold M. Schwartz
Louise Shiffer
Leonard Simmen
Singer Design Staff
Abel Sorensen
Kipp Stewart
Robert Summo
The Svedberg
Alf Svensson

Pipsan Saarinen Swanson
Maurizio Tempestini
Herbert Ten Have
Angelo Testa
Azalea S. Thorpe
Gerald Thurston
Dick Tremulis
Homer Tremulis
Paavo Tynell
Arthur Umanoff
Hendrik Van Keppel
John Van Koert
Paolo Venini

Kurt Versen
Arne Vodder
Poul M. Volther
Hans J. Wegner
Lyda Weyl
David G. Whitcomb
Edward J Wormley
Frank Lloyd Wright
Russel Wright
Zanuso
Dave Zeese

PHOTOGRAPHERS

Elmer Astleford
Arthur Avedon
G. Barrows
Kalman J. Chany
Colten & Siegler
George D. Cowdery
Eddystone Mfg. Company
Ernemac Photo. Service
Lionel Freedman
Maurey Garber
Alexandre Georges
Allan Gould
Idaka
The Illustrators

Kaufmann & Fabry Co.
Philip Mazzurco
McLaughlin & Guye
Stephen Michael
Miehlmann
Michael Miller
Marc Neuhof
Emilie Danielson Nicholson
Photographic Illustrators, Inc.
Dennis Purse
Rebman
james h reed
Fred Rola
Dale Rooks

Walter Rosenblum
David Royter
Ben Schnall
Stanley Simmons
Dean Stone &
    Hugo Steccati
Strüwing
Carl Ullrich, Inc.
Hans Van Nes
Aldo Vinai
Frank Willming
Thomas Yee